Clocks and Watches

1400-1900

ERIC BRUTON

FREDERICK A. PRAEGER, *Publishers*
New York · Washington

BOOKS THAT MATTER

Published in the United States of America in 1967
by Frederick A. Praeger, Inc., Publishers
111 Fourth Avenue, New York, N.Y. 10003
Second printing, 1967

Copyright © 1967 by Eric Bruton

Library of Congress Catalog Card Number : 67—14706

Printed in Great Britain

Contents

List of Illustrations

Plates

Fine bracket clock of the Queen Anne period by Thomas Tompion
frontispiece

between pages 96 and 97

List of Illustrations

Line Illustrations

Preface and Acknowledgements

THIS book is not a presentation of new research into horology nor even an exploration of controversial theories. It is the factual story of the development of clocks and watches from the earliest days until the present century, I hope, in clear and unequivocal language which includes the latest information on origins of inventions and dating of changes in design. It is intended primarily for beginners, particularly those with a latent interest in horology beyond the furniture aspects, but also for those whose knowledge may be specialized in one or other related field.

As such a long period of time, from about 1400 to 1900, is covered, it has been necessary to condense parts of the story in order to expand other parts describing timepieces that the reader is more likely to come across within the limits of his purse.

In the last decade there has been a sharp rise of interest in horology, and consequently prices have increased, so that many pieces within reach before are now available only to the rich or the museums. Fortunately, there still remain plenty of clocks and watches awaiting 'discovery' for modest outlays.

Purists may object to the fact that the book contains information about timekeepers ranging in price from over £10,000 to a mere pound, and that it extends too far into modern times – much too recent to attract the 'true' collector. This is deliberate because cash value is not the motivation of every collector; some are more interested in technical development and place a higher collecting value on, say, an incomplete, even damaged, unorthodox movement than on a complete clock in mint condition, but without technical merit. The greatest collector of all, the late Courtenay A. Ilbert, often took this view.

Unusual for a book of this type is the inclusion for comparison of some items, not regarded as collectors' pieces, because they might be mistaken for fine clocks by an unpracticed eye, and of early machine-made clocks and watches, although their appeal is quite different from that of the hand-made article. At an exhibition of captured arms during the war, I remember seeing an Englishman seize on a German-made booby device that had been machined and finished to the same quality as a precision clock, while an American made a bee-line for an extremely ingenious Japanese wire and plastics grenade, for which a clever production engineer had obviously been responsible. Almost together, they exclaimed, 'What a beautiful piece of work!' The second kind of appeal is a relatively new one among collectors, but is bound to grow as the hand-made articles of the past gradually become less available.

Fortunately, however, there are still many eighteenth as well as early nineteenth century clocks and watches to be found in this country at prices, within range of the average pocket, mainly because collectors in the past have neglected them because of their humble use, as in the case of the cottage clock and the common longcase clock, or their too recent provenance. How long this situation will exist can only be guessed. It may not be long, because collectors in other countries, particularly the United States of America, are clearing our 'stocks'. Many thousands of ordinary longcase clocks have been shipped in the last few years to the USA.

As far as I know, the facts as set out in this book are accurate. Philip Coole, of the British Museum, whose knowledge of and skill at horology is exceptional, pointed out a number of flaws in the manuscript text when he took considerable trouble in reading it, and I am pleased to acknowledge his assistance. If, however, any errors remain, the responsibility is mine.

Finally I would like to thank those who have helped with the pictures, some of whom sent me photographs a long time ago with permission to publish. They are: Mr William Hutton, of Smiths Industries (Clock and Watch Division) for permission to use some of the many pictures taken in the past by Smiths photographic unit, i.e. Plates 3, 8, 12, 31, 37, 38, 44, 45, 71, 79, 100, 101, 106, and 110; Sothebys, the famous auctioneers for Plates 5, 13, 19, 23, 77, 78, 83, 84, 85, 87, and 95; N. A. G. Press Ltd, London, W.C.2 for Plates 41, 55, 66, 75, 80, 92, and 93; Dr F. A. B. Ward of the Science Museum, for Plates 63, 68, and 105; Dr R. Vaudrey Mercer, of Cookham, Berks., for Plates 80, 104, and 108; Charles Terwilliger, of the Horolovar Co., New York, for Plates 47 and 48; T. P. Camerer-Cuss, of London, W.C.2, for Plates 61, and 62; J. Lowy, of Melbourne, Australia, for Plates 42, and 54; Mallet and Son (Antiques) Ltd, of London, W.1, for the Frontispiece; Philip P. Thornton of Great Haywood, Stafford, for Plate 72; the Basingstoke Museum for Plate 76; the Antiquarian Horological Society, of London, E.C.2, for Plate 6; H. Carter Bowles, of Cheltenham, for Plate 7; Ernest L. Edwardes, of Sale, Cheshire, for Plate 10; P. J. Forde, of Saltney Ferry, nr. Chester, for Plate 32; Pearson Page Jewsbury Co., of Birmingham, for Plate 57; the Mauthe Museum, Black Forest, W. Germany, for Plate 65; Ingersoll Ltd, of London, for Plate 91; J. D. Owen, of Didsbury Park, Manchester, for Plate 2; the Chelsea Antiques Fair authorities for Plate 58, showing an exhibit by W. A. Pinn, Dunstable; the International Antiques Fair authorities for Plate 59, showing an exhibit by J. P. Hagnauer, of Paris, and Charles Allix for letting me photograph some of his clocks.

Great Bookham, Surrey   *Eric Bruton*

1 Monastic Clocks

TIME is one of the three fundamental quantities on which all physical science is based and its measurement has been the concern of every developing civilization. Yet the inventor of the mechanical clock it unknown. There is not even any degree of certainty about where is was invented and when, except that its origin was in Europe at some time towards the end of the thirteenth century.

Nature's clock is the sun, so an early name for the mechanical timekeeper was the 'artificial clock' to distinguish it from a 'natural' one. This neatly pinpoints the function of any timepiece: to imitate the apparent daily passage of the sun. When the sun shone in the Middle Ages – and it shone more frequently before the First Industrial Revolution generated a permanent smoke haze over the country – it was sufficient normally to note the time by the sun's position in the sky. The hours were marked by its travel from east to west, and most easily noted by a shadow scale or sundial. From Saxon days until relatively recent times in England, sundials were commonly placed in public places to mark the 'tides', into which the Saxons divided their days, and later the hours. We still occasionally speak of 'noontide' and 'eventide'.

The function of the artificial clock was to show where a shadow would fall if the sun were obscured, to give the time at night and inside buildings. The first clockmaker's problem was to make a hand or a dial rotate at the same rate as the sun appeared to move across the sky. The hand of an early table clock revolving once in 24 hours over a horizontal dial will in fact follow the sun across the sky. How to make such a device was not so simple.

It has been suggested in recent times that the clock is a descendant of mechanical models made by astronomers to demonstrate theories of the movements of the heavenly bodies. From the few specimens and documents that remain, it is certain that many such models were built and that some were exceedingly complex. At first they were hand-operated, but the advantages of automatic operation must soon have become evident as there is an elaborate record written in AD 1090 of astronomical spheres and globes and timetellers in ancient China driven slowly and steadily by the power of falling water. Astronomical models were made in other parts of the old world, including Europe, where the power of a falling weight was employed instead of water. At some point, the mechanism that rotated the model at a fixed rate was separated and became a valuable instrument in its own right – a clock.

Even the first clock was the combination of several inventions, some old, some new. It comprised a suspended weight to provide a driving force, a train of gear wheels to transmit the power and to turn a dial to indicate the time, a time-controlling device to regulate the falling weight, and a link between the time controller and the rest of the mechanism known as an 'escapement'.

The time controller was, and still is, almost invariably an oscillating or vibrating system. The earliest, called a foliot, was a horizontal bar with a weight at each end (Plate 1) which swung slowly to and fro. Almost as early or perhaps contemporary with the first foliot was the balance wheel which also swung to and fro. After mid-seventeenth century the pendulum became the most common time controller.

The first escapement in use was the crown wheel and verge (Plate 1) the action of which is described in a later chapter. It was such a successful arrangement that it was not superseded completely for six hundred years. The time controller combined with the escapement of any timekeeper measures out the power supplied by the driving weight or spring into tiny doses. It allows the power to escape at short intervals of time. It actually stops and restarts the clock continually. This is a feature of almost every type of escapement. For example, the movement ('movement' is the correct name for the mechanism) of a longcase clock is released every second, for a fraction of a second, so that all the hands move in a series of little jumps. The tick is the sound of the whole system of gears supporting the weight being brought to a sudden stop after being momentarily released. Similarly the hands of a master or slave clock in a large building are moved in jumps every half a minute and the hands of a man's wrist watch jump every fifth of a second. Yet people continue to be amazed that watches and clocks going continuously in little jerks day and night without cease for year after year ever need lubrication or servicing and, indeed, ever wear out!

It seems reasonably certain that monasteries were the earliest regular users of alarms, which were a primitive form of clock. The word 'clock' is derived from the same source as the French *cloche* and Teutonic *Glocke*, meaning bell, and to be pedantic we should use, even today, the word 'timepiece' for a device that tells the time only, and 'clock' for an alarm, or striking clock. Unfortunately the recorders in ancient monasteries used the word *horologium* for all kinds of timekeepers – clocks, sundials, water clocks, and sand glasses – which has confused the history of the mechanical clock.

In the Middle Ages, monasteries scattered across Europe were complete communities, like villages with granaries, mills, potteries, and workshops, clustered around a central church. These colonies of monks lived according to a strictly ordered routine to make sure Satan could find no mischief for idle hands to do. It is therefore no wonder that Cassiodorus, the hermit of Monte Cassino, who made sundials and water clocks, wrote that timekeepers were 'invented for the utmost benefit of the human race' and that the Benedictine Order established on the mountain set out times for work and times for prayer to be announced by the ringing of a bell. In the twelfth century, the rules of the monastery at Cluny made it the duty of the sacristan to keep the time and to ring the bell which marked the canonical hours.

There is, still preserved, a complaint by Bishop Alnwick to Dorchester Abbey that 'in the said monastery no fixed hour is observed for rising to matins by night and this because the horologium which should strike all the hours by day and night is not kept in good condition.' He grumbled that the sacristan had deliberately converted the ropes of the clock to other purposes.

At that time, day and night were thought of as entirely separate entities; we still have no separate word in English for the period of 24 hours. Civilized countries of the time divided time into 12 hours of light and 12 hours of darkness – from sunrise to sunset and from sunset to sunrise. These are called 'temporal hours', or 'unequal hours', because the length of an hour varied. Artificial light was so poor at the time that natural light literally controlled the period of human activity. Early civilizations developed in the Mediterranean, where the periods of night and day were about the same and did not vary through the year, but when learning spread northwards, the differences in temporal hours became more marked. In London, for example, the 12 temporal hours of day and the 12 of night could vary from $7\frac{3}{4}$ to $16\frac{1}{2}$ of our present 'equal hours', according to the time of year.

From early times, astronomers used a 24 hours system for their day and, from the fourteenth century, the introduction of mechanical clocks caused a gradual change-over to 24 hours of equal lengths, although some communities clung to the primitive systems of unequal hours for centuries longer – Japan into the nineteenth century. There were inevitable local variations. In the fourteenth century, Italy counted her 24 hours from sundown, which involved altering the rate of the clock; Nuremberg made the old temporal hours of equal length, but had two counts, one from dawn and the other from dusk. Basle started the day at midday, but called it one o'clock! Muslims used, and still do, 24 equal hours, but varied their starting point. In England the day was counted in two sets of 12 equal hours starting at noon and midnight, a system which most of Europe had adopted before the fifteenth century opened.

There was need in the fourteenth century to call burghers from the townships for civil duties, to serve in the militia, to help rebuild town walls or harvest the town fields. Town and city councils resented having to depend upon religious communities and to be restricted to ringing of the canonical hours for their timekeeping and soon public bells began to appear. The bell was looked after by a clock-keeper with an alarm to indicate when his big bell should be rung. One important sounding was for curfew, when everyone had to be indoors. In Italy, particularly, many bell towers were erected for this purpose.

A record dated 1286 refers to a daily allowance of a loaf of bread for the clock-keeper, Bartholomo Orologario, at old St Paul's in London. It was the duty of some of these clock-keepers to ring the bell every hour, a task which meant keeping awake. It seems that reliable clock-keepers were not numerous and there arose a demand for clocks big enough to strike the big bells themselves. In other words, for the man to be superseded by the machine. This was taken literally by the mechanicians of the time, who constructed big clocks to operate mechanical men to strike the big bells. In 1410, for example, the Montpellier town council recorded dissatisfaction with their clock-keeper and decided to order from Dijon one of the new-fangled clocks which did not need a human keeper.

The robot figures operated by the clocks were usually made of wood and painted to look like men-at-arms, perhaps because they always obeyed orders. They were called 'jacomarts', which today has become contracted to 'clock jacks'. The expression 'roasting jack' comes from the same source. Not all large clocks employed jacks to strike their bells and not all had dials.

A number of these clocks still exist around Europe, most having been altered at some time. The oldest still going is in Salisbury Cathedral. Originally made in 1386 to strike the hours only, it stood neglected and unrecognized for its antiquity in the cathedral tower for many years. In 1931 it was cleaned and put on show and in 1956 a carefully made reproduction of its original verge and foliot escapement was fitted instead of the pendulum to which it had been converted in its later history. (Plate 1.)

There are two other clocks nearly as old as Salisbury's, one at Rouen in France and the other from Wells in England. The Salisbury and Wells clocks are exceptionally alike; indeed it was this fact that led to the recognition of the old movement at Salisbury by T. R. Robinson in 1929 as being one of the oldest if not the oldest still extant. The Wells movement (now in the Science Museum) operated automata which are still at Wells Cathedral but worked by a later clock. There is a display of fighting knights at the hour. A jack, named Jack Blandifer, strikes the hours on a bell with a hammer and sounds the quarters with his heels. Also operated by the Wells movement was a model of the universe according to Medieval ideas of creation, perhaps an illustration of the fact that the domestic clock is 'a fallen angel from the astronomer's heaven'.

Both Salisbury and Wells clocks were most likely commissioned by Bishop Erghum, a foreigner consecrated at Bruges, who was at Salisbury from 1375 to 1388 and was translated to Bath and Wells in 1388, remaining there until 1400. He probably employed the three 'orologiers' named Johannes Vrieman, Willelmus Vrieman, and Johannes Lietuyt, all from Delft in the Netherlands, who were invited in 1368 by King Edward III to practise their craft in England. It is likely that the monk named Peter Lightfoot, credited in a number of books with constructing our earliest clocks, was a mythical figure whose name was an anglicized version of Lietuyt.

2 Great Clocks

MANY large medieval clocks still exist; undoubtedly there are some that await discovery too, in old churches and towers in England and on the continent. They were once called 'great clocks'. The current name is 'tower', or 'turret', clocks. All such early clocks were made of wrought iron, and the members of the frames were held together by iron wedges driven through slots in tenon joints, like early wooden furniture. Screws, nuts, and bolts were never used, although they may be seen today on some old tower clock movements, having been added during a repair or replacement of worn parts, or during conversion to pendulum operation, a common operation after the pendulum clock was invented in 1657.

The corner posts of the earliest turret clocks were similar in form to cathedral buttresses and at times were set at an angle of 45° as can be seen in Plate 1. Some had bold finials at the tops of the corner posts. Toothed wheels usually engaged with lantern pinions, that is, small gear wheels made up of two plates united by a series of rods like a cage. One can also be seen in Plate 1. It is not absolutely certain that lantern pinions are a sign of very early clocks, however, as they may have been replacements. Clock makers continued to use them for cheapness on clocks made in the Black Forest of Germany and they are employed even today by some American firms in alarms for the same reason. The spokes of the large toothed wheels were lapped to both sides of the rim and fire welded by blacksmiths. The arbors, as clockmakers call the shafts, were octagonal.

Later clocks with these so-called 'birdcage frames' are lighter and weaker in construction and the corner posts less frequently set at an angle. The corner posts have shallow mouldings and curve outwards with a knob end. Around 1600 the knob changed to a double-curved shape (ogee) then to a pointed ball and finally to a bun. Corner posts became round and from the eighteenth century and into the

20

nineteenth as late as the 1880s, a tower clock frame of this type so had the look of a Victorian bed with its ornamental knobs on the posts, that it is called a 'bedpost frame'.

Installation of the movement for 'Big Ben' in 1858 introduced into England a new design of turret clock movement which originated in France and is called the 'horizontal frame', in which all the wheels and arbors are set in a line like the road wheels of a railway engine.

Design of the first large clocks to be set up in England undoubtedly came from the continent of Europe, but some local makers, probably blacksmiths, tried their hands at clockmaking and developed a type of their own with a fundamentally different frame and layout. The frame was a vertical beam with the wheels laid out in a line (Plate 2). There appear to have been two areas of activity, the West Country where iron frames were in favour, and the Midlands where the choice was wood. It is not generally known that the timekeeping part of the old Exeter Cathedral clock is built on these domestic lines. The period of this offshoot work was from about 1490 to 1550. Examples can be seen at Cothele House, at Calstock, Cornwall, (which belongs to the National Trust) where the clock has its original verge and foliot, and is going again, and in the tower of Sydling St Nicholas Church in Dorset, where a vertical frame clock is still working. A list is given in Appendix 1. There are probably others still to be discovered.

The weights of old turret clocks were often of stone. Winding was performed by turning a four-spoked handwheel, sometimes with a rim like a car steering-wheel (Plate 1) attached to a wooden barrel on which the rope carrying the weight was wound. Stone weights and this laborious method of winding persisted for about three centuries and their presence is not indicative of great age. Many clocks were converted to gear winding by providing a gear wheel instead of a handwheel on the barrel, which was wound by a toothed pinion turned by a handle, to make the clock-winder's task easier.

Unfortunately large numbers of these magnificent old wrought-iron turret clocks have been allowed to rust away or given to scrap merchants, although there must still be a number lying around in dark corners around the country, waiting to be discovered. Certainly there are many still to be appreciated in old churches and the clergy have been alerted to such unsuspected treasures by the Council for the Preservation of Old Churches, even if not all have taken action. One very small turret clock converted to pendulum from foliot was found in 1964 in a dustbin in London by Mr P. G. Coole, a member of the British Museum staff!

Most of these old clocks had striking mechanisms. The striking train of gears in a clock is quite separate from the time-keeping train of gears. It has its own driving weight to operate the hammer or jack which strikes the hours on a bell. At every hour, the timekeeping part of the clock releases the striking part, which strikes the appropriate number of blows then locks itself until it is released at the next hour. The number of blows struck by the hammer is controlled by a disc with a series of notches in the edge called a 'locking plate', or more correctly a 'count wheel'. That on the Salisbury clock can be seen on the left of Plate 1.

Readers interested in early tower clocks should beware of the dates ascribed to some still preserved in churches. For example, the fine astronomical clock in the church of Ottery St Mary in Devon was probably made at some time near the end of the sixteenth century, but has been provided with a mythical history and wrongly dated 1327. The movement is one of the later weak birdcages made during Elizabethan or later years. Again, the Wimborne Minster clock, claimed to have been made in the fourteenth century by 'Peter Lightfoot' was in fact made in the eighteenth by William Monk, of Berwick St John, Wiltshire, who made the Sherborne Abbey clock in 1740. Unfortunately the Sherborne clock has recently been converted to electric mains operation and original parts destroyed.

All this goes to show that you should never take the age of a clock on trust. The examination of these ancient clocks and the records relating to them, their comparison with ancient clocks on the continent, and the attempt to date them accurately, led to acrid and bitter exchanges, even – and this is almost unbelievable – to some faking of the evidence pointing to earlier dates for the clocks.

The earliest clock in England still performing as a timekeeper is probably that in Rye church in Sussex, made in 1515. (Salisbury clock is now a showpiece.) The Rye clock has been converted to pendulum control, the pendulum being 16 feet 6 inches long so that it takes $2\frac{1}{4}$ seconds to swing from one side to the other. The wooden pendulum rod has a crosstree and stays, as if it had been made in a boatyard, and hangs down to swing in the body of the church over the aisle.

Nearly all earlier clocks were converted from foliot to pendulum operation from the end of the seventeenth century onwards. This involved turning the escapement through 90 degrees which left evidence of the alteration by holes in the frames.

Large early clocks have been described in some detail as they have been much neglected by collectors. Most that still exist are in the hands of churches and should not be available to the collector (although some have passed out of ecclesiastical possession through ignorance of local church authorities in arranging replacement of their clocks). There are others, however, used originally as time-keepers for large estates and not infrequently sited above the stables, or by commercial concerns, which may be legitimately acquired.

The first domestic clocks looked like scaled-down versions of large tower or turret clocks, made of iron, hung on the wall and driven by weights. Usually they struck a bell at the hours and often had an alarm which could be set when required. From about 1400, for well over a century, they were so expensive they could only be purchased by kings and princes and the very wealthiest families. The posses-sion of a clock, then, must have been equivalent to possessing a millionaire's yacht today.

CLOCKMAKING NATIONS

Domestic iron clocks in use in England were almost all imported from the continent and are known today as 'chamber clocks' or 'Gothic clocks' (Plate 3). Around 1550, brass came rapidly into use and later the first English clocks, lantern-shaped and made mostly of brass, driven by weights and controlled by balance wheel. Lantern clocks, or 'brass clocks' as they were called at the time, became cheaper and their use spread deeper through society during the sixteenth and seventeenth centuries. The Germans, who specialized in iron clocks, faked table clocks to look like brass. After more sophisticated clocks appeared on the scene, lantern clocks continued to be made by local clockmakers for farming and developing indus-trial communities as the need for timekeeping became more urgent. Lantern clocks with pendulums were still being produced in this century.

While England was turning out brass weight-driven clocks in the sixteenth century, the continent was exploiting a new invention made about 1430 – the spring drive – for clocks, particularly the Duchy of Burgundy. The spring was not as effective as a weight because its power varied.

HISTORY SUMMARIZED

To help visualize the development of the domestic timekeeper, its subsequent history is summarized here in a few paragraphs before expanding in subsequent chapters the aspects of interest to collectors.

England's first domestic clocks were the iron clocks referred to above. The first essentially English production was the lantern clock (Plate 9) made mostly of brass and driven by weights.

In the meantime the continent of Europe was exploiting a new invention, the spring-driven clock. It heralded the portable timekeeper, which before the end of that century had become small enough to be carried on the person – in other words to become a watch. By the later sixteenth and early seventeenth century the South Germans had developed a substantial export trade in spring-driven timepieces. The French were very active also, but concentrated more on quality, and there were industries in other countries, particularly Italy.

The next landmark was the invention of the pendulum clock in Holland in 1657, which improved timekeeping very substantially. It was taken up most rapidly in England which for the next century became the dominant clock and watchmaking country.

Before the pendulum, most domestic clocks had only hour hands. Afterwards two hands became commonplace. The minute hands, even seconds hands, on continental clocks of the time were more affectations for the rich.

Not much later, about 1675, the hairspring was invented for watches, which gave watchmaking the same kind of impetus the pendulum had given to clockmaking. By chance the waistcoat came into fashion at about the same time and owners began to carry watches in their waistcoat pockets instead of on a cord round their necks or hanging from their belts, as previously.

From these times there were steady decorative and technical improvements (and at times degeneration), one often affecting the other, but all clocks and watches were more or less craft made.

During the early nineteenth century, the methods of the hand craftsmen and specialist makers were finally all but submerged by machine making and batch assembly. English clockmakers stopped making parts themselves and bought clock movements in quantity from firms such as Thwaites and Reed, of Clerkenwell, and Handley and Moore, of Birmingham, and watch movements from the many

24

makers in Clerkenwell and Lancashire, or from abroad, which they fitted into cases bought elsewhere.

They still continued the tradition of having their names engraved on the movements and engraved or painted on the dials. For example, hundreds of clocks like that in Plate 30 were made all with different names engraved on the back plate of the clock. Often on one edge of a plate a number can be found stamped, giving the serial number and date of manufacture by the true makers. Many famous genuine makers took advantage of this supply service for 'bread and butter' lines while continuing to make special and high quality clocks themselves.

The situation eventually arose when many of those who had their names on dials were retailers only, particularly in the later nineteenth century. This explains why, even today, retailers still call themselves clock*makers* and watch*makers*.

3 First Domestic Clocks

DURING the latter part of the Renaissance, when the great revival of the arts included what we call today 'the sciences', most inventive and decorative genius was to be found on the continent of Europe. The twin towns of Augsburg and Nuremberg in South Germany, in particular, became manufacturing centres on very sophisticated lines for the sixteenth century. The French had manufacturing industries around Blois; the Italians were active too, although very few early Italian clocks have survived. Denmark was a centre of 'research', by a group of thinkers and mechanicians including clockmaker Jobst Burgi around the astronomer Tycho Brahe. They were concerned with improving timekeeping accuracy, which was vital for more accurate astronomical observations.

It was on the continent that the mainspring drive was developed. The skill of blacksmiths was needed for tower and chamber clock construction; spring clocks demanded the skill of locksmiths who were practised in making metals springy by tempering steel and hammering non-ferrous metals, a process we now call 'work hardening'. For their first spring-driven designs, makers favoured table clocks of drum or canister shape or like square boxes which stood on three or four small feet and had their dials on the tops of the cases (Plates 4 and 5). Very few English makers followed suit. The cases were almost invariably of metal and highly decorated.

A decoration of table clocks made in Germany was a cast scene showing many animals against a background of trees and mountains (Plate 5). A few humans were included with the elephant, lion, unicorn, camel, ram, monkeys, etc. The side of the clock on which the scene occurs was made in a strip and joined. It appears from a study of the few clocks that still exist that there must have been a specialist at the time supplying decorative strip—batch production methods in the 1500s.

Table clocks had a fusee or stackfreed (described on pages 100 to 104) to even out the varying power of the mainspring, and a wheel or dumb-bell shaped balance. Some gave elaborate planetary indications as well as the time of day. Clocks made in Germany and Italy had a single hand showing the time over a dial marked I to XII and 13 to 24 hours, but not those made in France or Britain. Not infrequently, knobs were placed at the hour chapters around the dial so that the owner could note the time in the dark by feeling the position of the hand in relation to the knobs. Plate 76 shows a watch with such a dial and knobs. It was a lengthy task at the time to create an artificial light.

Another form of early spring clock was much smaller than the table clock. It was hexagonal in shape and taller than it was wide, like a small tower with a domed top. These clocks were usually French or Flemish. The brass cases were elaborately engraved and the domed top, which concealed a bell, was surrounded by finials or carved frets. A few tabernacle-style clocks but with four instead of six sides were made in England; one still extant was by Bartholomew Newsam and is dated about 1568.

The frames of both larger and these small table clocks were built from vertical pillars with horizontal plates so that the wheels were horizontal. The small clock movements were in two tiers which gave them their height.

The town of Augsburg also made elaborate brass-cased clocks with vertical corner pillars but they had vertical plates and straps to take the wheel bearings like lantern clocks, so that the wheels were in a vertical plane.

AUGSBURG CLOCKS

A monumental type of Augsburg clocks of the period was particularly distinctive, as shown in Plate 7. Made during the sixteenth and early seventeenth century, these became so popular during the late nineteenth that the firm of Haas and Co. made electrotype copies of the originals in some numbers and anyone coming across such a 'treasure' should make sure that it is not one of the copies. These 'Türmchen-Uhr' had beautiful and elaborate decoration and many dials giving such information as the phases of the moon, the age of the moon, star time as well as solar time, the day of the month, the positions of the sun and the moon in the zodiac, and the positions of the sun, moon, and certain stars in the heavens. Despite the primitive form of time controller, some very complex differo-epicyclic gearing and advanced gear ratio calculations were incorporated.

Augsburg also turned out many novelty clocks in the sixteenth century and later, the most general form being based on the table clock with an animated figure or figures on top. Sometimes the clock cases were made of wood but the automata were always of metal. There was a huge variety of such clocks—in fact the variety of the Augsburg clock production during the Renaissance was almost unbelievable – and a favourite was an animal such as a lion, griffon, dog, elephant, or cow with blinking eyes, the eyes being connected to the swinging balance (Plate 6).

Some automata clocks were extremely elaborate, resembling, for example, coach and horses, which drove the entire clock a short distance across the table when the clock struck, as well as operating displays of human figures. Another version was a nef, or ship on wheels, with moving guns and figures. These models were large, two feet or more in length, and made of brass or brass and wood, with sometimes a chime or tunes on organ pipes. It must have been the biggest 'gimmick' of a sixteenth-century grand banquet to have a clock like a ship that drove itself down the centre of the table at the hour to musical accompaniment and animated display on the decks, especially when the people who attended banquets marvelled as much at the magic of mechanics as they do now at the magic of electronics.

Another form of clock from Augsburg was the monstrance or mirror clock, so-called because of its shape, a base with a pillar holding the circular dial. The dial was often surrounded by elaborate fretwork and sometimes a human figure was used instead of a plain pillar. Crucifix clocks are also of the period, although these and monstrance clocks were made well into the eighteenth century. A crucifix clock shows Christ on the cross with a small clock incorporated in the base or on the top of the cross (Plate 8).

In Augsburg clocks, including those with automata (animated figures), a revolving dial was often employed with a fixed hand, but the dial was a band, drum, or sphere with numerals engraved round the equator, which revolved. This system, shown in Plate 8, became very popular again in the nineteenth century during the Industrial Revolution when more people were interested in mechanical devices and the French clockmaking industry was in the ascendancy. Fixed dials were also employed, of course, as in one Augsburg clock in the British Museum in which a farmer's figure revolves to point to the time on a horizontal dial, while watched by a blinking-eye cow being milked by a milkmaid. At each stroke of the hour, the milkmaid draws a squirt of real milk into a bucket!

LANTERN CLOCKS

In the meantime only a few clockmakers were at work in England. One, a Flamand, made the table clock in Plate 4. There was not a truly English-styled product until the lantern clock made its appearance around 1600; it was still being made as late as the twentieth century. The lantern clock is said to be named because of its likeness in appearance to the old candle lantern with horn windows, but its name is more likely to be a corruption of 'latten', meaning 'brass'. For the first ten or twenty years it was made of iron, however, like the imported continental chamber or Gothic clocks from which it was copied. Then brass became more usual for most parts, including the corner posts, dial, and wheels, and the clock was called at the time 'a brass clock'.

A lantern clock always has a posted frame (with a post at each corner, like the early church clocks) but with brass posts of circular section. The movement, unlike that of some Gothic clocks was enclosed. The 'case' of the lantern clock comprises the top and bottom plates by which the corner posts are united, the dial on the front, two side doors made of brass, and an iron plate at the back. The clock stands on four feet, extensions of the corner pillars, which also carry tall finials at their tops. The finials hold an X-shaped bracket from which is suspended the bell, with a fifth finial on top of the bell. To fill the space below the bell the top edges are fitted with decorative brass frets. A pair of dolphins was the most favoured design, but foliage and heraldic motifs were also employed. A typical lantern clock is shown in Plate 9.

Lantern clocks were weight-driven, one weight being needed for the timekeeping side, another for the striking, and a third for the alarm when this was fitted. Most English lantern clocks had hour-striking. Each weight hung on a rope which passed over a grooved pulley and had a smaller counterweight attached to the other end to keep the rope in the pulley. In later lantern clocks a chain was used, usually the endless rope or chain described on page 98. Most earlier ones were converted.

To wind the clock, the free end of each rope is pulled in turn to raise the weights. The height of the clock off the ground and the length of the rope determines how long it will run without stopping. Most lantern clocks would run for about twelve hours as they were placed about 9 ft. high, but some earlier ones were only made to run for about six or eight hours.

Lantern clocks were made originally with an hour hand only, and in consequence the dial was engraved with the hours and the quarters, i.e. with *four* engraved divisions between the hours. The engraved scale was inside the circle of Roman numerals, which is called the 'chapter ring'. Two hands seen on a lantern clock usually mean that the minute hand, and the gears to operate it (the 'motion work') were added in the eighteenth century or later. If there are no minute divisions on the dial, the minute hand was certainly added later. Even if there *are* minute divisions on the dial of a lantern clock with two hands, it is possible that the dial was changed at the time the minute hand was added or later. When minute divisions appear on a dial, they are engraved on the outside edge of the chapter ring – *five* between each hour, of course.

The very earliest single hour hands were shaped with an arrow-head point, an oval central boss, and a long tail. In the centre of the boss was a square hole which fitted over a square on the arbor through the centre of the dial, the hand being retained by a tapered pin through a hole. The tail was to set the alarm (see page 118) and had another use. To alter the time shown by the hand, it has to be turned against a friction clutch; a short, stubby hand becomes easier to turn by using a finger on the hand and thumb on the tail.

Soon the points each side of the arrow-head became loops and the loops became elaborated. The tail became shorter, and the central boss became round. Eventually the square hole in the boss changed to a circular one with a notch in it. The series of changes is shown in Fig. 1.

All lantern clocks before about 1600 and many afterwards had a balance wheel control. The balance wheel, with a single spoke, was situated under the bell and was almost the same diameter (Plate 10). It was operated by a crown wheel and verge escapement. (Described on pages 92–5.) After about 1660 most lantern clocks were made with pendulums and some of the old balance wheel clocks were converted to pendulum operation. Such pendulums were short in length and hung behind and outside the brass case. Lantern clocks with their original balance wheels are now extremely rare and those converted to short pendulum operation are also hardly to be found.

30

Occasionally during this period a lantern clock was made with a short pendulum which hung in the centre of the clock. The pendulum bob was banana-shaped instead of being like a small pear, and on each side of the clock was a wedge-of-pie shaped wing into which the ends of the pendulum could be seen swinging. These are known as 'winged lantern clocks'. The wings originally had glass or transparent horn fronts.

After the long pendulum of about 39 inches became popular with its associated anchor escapement of about 1670, many lantern clocks were converted to anchor and pendulum, the ungainly pendulum hanging down the back. Large numbers of the old balance wheel

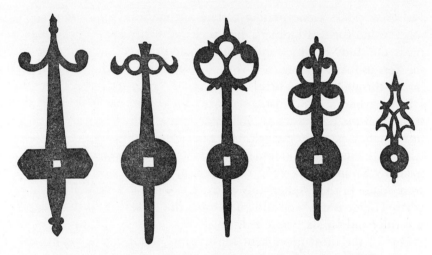

FIG. I. Development of the lantern clock hand, earliest on the left.

lantern clocks were converted to long pendulum because of the astonishing improvement in timekeeping.

The early lantern clocks were hung from a hook on the wall by means of a semi-circular iron stirrup at the top of the back of the clock. To hold the clock away from the wall, to keep the weights clear, and also to prevent it from being moved while it was being wound, there were two pointed spurs or distance pieces attached to the iron plate, or feet, at the back, which dug into the wall. The stirrups and spurs were omitted from later lantern clocks as it became the fashion to stand the clock on an oaken shelf, with holes in it for the weight lines, fastened to the wall. Lantern clocks with long pendulums are sometimes seen standing on a pyramid-shaped stand made of oak boards which enclose the pendulum and weights. Such stands were made at almost any later date.

Lantern clocks were made in Germany and in France as well, often retaining their iron construction, although some of brass were produced. An indication of a continental brass clock is that the terminals and feet were made in one piece with the pillars whereas they were usually separate in the English construction, as seen in Plate 9. One-piece construction can be seen in some English provincially-made lantern clocks.

PENDULUM INVENTION

Elaborate clocks incorporating certain astronomical indications had some value for astronomers, but their inexactitude as timekeepers made the study of timekeeping one of the principal occupations of thinkers in many countries. The man responsible for the first major 'break-through' was Christiaan Huygens (1629–95), the famous Dutch astronomer and mathematician, who wrote the first accurate treatise on the pendulum as well as designing and having made the first practical pendulum clock. Huygens' clock, still preserved in the Christiaan Huygens Museum at Leyden in Holland, was a wall clock made by Salomon Coster in 1657 (Fig. 15). Clocks of several types were made in the Netherlands at the time, but it was in England, where Huygens was well known to other thinkers, that the invention was fully and rapidly exploited.

One of the most prominent makers in London at the time was Ahasuerus Fromanteel, a man of Dutch extraction. He was among the first to hear that Salomon Coster, in The Hague, was making a new kind of clock for Huygens. Being a man of exceptional enterprise and business acumen, he sent a young member of his family, John, to be apprenticed to Coster, only eleven days after the patent was granted, to learn the secret of making pendulum clocks. As soon as 1658, Ahasuerus Fromanteel was advertising pendulum clocks for sale and there is evidence that Huygens approved of the arrangement. The pendulum was so successful in England that in a very short time nearly all London makers had adopted it. The speed at which knowledge of it spread was remarkable for a time when it could take half a century for an idea to cross the country.

The most common clock in England then was the brass lantern clock, with a sprinkling of table and tabernacle clocks made in the country, imported German and French clocks, and the earlier imported iron chamber clocks. Introduction of the pendulum caused a profound change. At about the same time, mid-seventeenth century, the wooden case was becoming a favourite with English clockmakers. This may have been due to the fact that they did not have the elaborate apprenticeships of the Bavarian clockmakers in Nuremberg and Augsburg and were not so well equipped to make their own decorated metal cases. Therefore they employed cabinet-makers, of

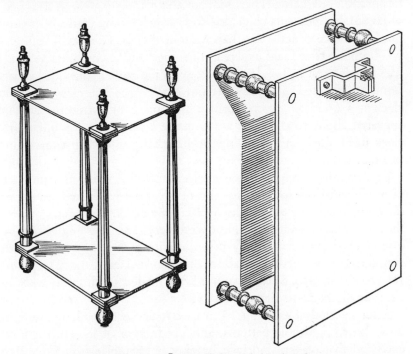

FIG. 2. The posted frame (left), and the plate frame.

whom there were many because of the furniture industry, for case-making.

Around this time a big change also took place in construction of the movement. In effect, the table clock was turned through 90 degrees, so that the pillars were horizontal and the plates and dial vertical. Fig. 2 shows the posted frame of the lantern clock compared with a plate frame of a longcase or of a bracket clock. A short pendulum about 10 inches long, with a small pear-shaped bob was favoured from the first, the clock being driven by spring or weight.

Taking weight-driven clocks first, the earliest were hung on the

c

wall, like lantern clocks, but had square dials and were enclosed in wooden cases, below which hung the weights. Some were wound by a cranked key through a hole in the dial instead of pulling on the ropes or chains to raise the weights. An example of the hanging or hooded wall clock is shown in Plate 11. This has an endless chain drive, invented by Huygens in 1657. The case is a removable wooden hood.

The years after mid-seventeenth century were a time of considerable development in furniture-making, particularly during the Restoration or Charles II period from about 1660 to 1690. A number of favourable elements coincided to encourage new forms of furniture and more orderly and harmonious design. Charles II himself was both interested and expert in horology and encouraged general scientific interest in London which, with the exuberance of ideas in furniture, resulted in a fresh form of clock – the longcase or coffin clock – a good timekeeper and a fine piece of furniture, which appeared about 1660. It did not become known as a 'grandfather' clock until much later, after the popular song using this expression in 1876.

The hanging weights were enclosed by the wooden trunk to protect them from interference and in effect the wall clock stood on the floor to become the tall case or longcase clock. Long cases before this time were not unknown, but were very rare. The English longcase clock grew very rapidly in popularity in many countries and continued in production for about one hundred and fifty years from 1660 to about 1820. Small numbers were made after this time and are occasionally hand-made even today.

After a period of searching from 1660 to about 1700, design settled down to recognizable patterns, and production of longcase clocks exceeded that of spring-driven bracket or mantel clocks from the English trade, which was based in London. After about 1750, the position changed and London concentrated on bracket clocks, leaving provincial makers to concentrate on longcases. After mid-eighteenth century, huge numbers of longcase clocks were made all over England, Scotland, Wales and Ireland, but especially in Yorkshire and Lancashire. Nearly all clocks by provincial makers date after 1760.

During the last twenty-five years or so, more and more machine-made parts were introduced, longcases became uglier, the painted dial superseded the brass dial and finally longcase clock production was almost entirely by machine.

4 Longcase Clocks

First longcases followed rather severe classical architectural styles, with △-shaped top like the Parthenon supported by a column at each side. The case itself was narrow and panelled, a door in the trunk being long and narrow and often with three panels, as shown in Plate 12. Early longcases were ebonized and only about six feet or six feet six inches tall. The base was only a little wider than the trunk at first, and most of the early clocks had feet, although they have disappeared from almost all the surviving examples.

The weights were wound up by a cranked key through holes in the dial. The dial was protected by a glass, a complete break from the earlier continental clocks. The glass was fixed to the top part – the hood – of the clock, which was raised upwards on a groove at the back when winding. A trigger called a 'spoon' just inside the door released the 'rising hood' so that the timekeeping could not be interfered with by anyone not possessing a key to the clock door.

An almost positive indication of an early longcase clock is the shape of the moulding underneath the hood. In the transition period when various experiments were made with styles, between 1660 and 1700, this was convex in shape. After 1700 or a few years later, the concave shape became universal. The two shapes can be compared in Plates 13 and 14.

In the meantime, cases had been growing in size, firstly because of the adoption of the long pendulum, which hung down into the trunk and had to have more space than the very narrow sizes permitted. There were experiments with very long pendulums about 60 inches long and beating $1\frac{1}{4}$ seconds instead of the one second of the 39-inch pendulum. Heights of cases grew to seven feet and more. Dials, just over eight inches square in the first longcase clocks, grew to ten inches.

It became more difficult with a taller clock for the owner to raise

35

the hood for winding, especially as people were shorter then, and not long before 1700 the glazed *door* for the dial was introduced. If it were necessary to attend to the movement itself, the hood, with its glass door, could be pulled forwards and removed. Early hoods often had glass in the sides as well, so that the movement could be seen, or frets of wood or brass backed by silk to allow the sound of the hour bell or chimes to escape.

Another feature of well-made clocks was a circular or oval-shaped glass – a 'lentille' – in the trunk door so that the swinging of the pendulum could be seen. This was perhaps more decorative than useful because the sound of the tick immediately indicated whether the clock was still going, and its real purpose was to show the owner's clock had the new long pendulum (Plate 14). Some clocks had pendulum apertures made from 'bullseyes', the thick central portion of a sheet of glass, made at the time by blowing a bulb, cutting off the top to form a cup, then spinning the blowtube to produce a circular sheet. These bullseyes are seen in old leaded lights. In clocks with $1\frac{1}{4}$-second pendulums, a pendulum aperture was sometimes provided in the plinth of the case, about a foot off the floor, and the plinth also had a door so that the pendulum could be adjusted.

The Royal pendulum, as the long pendulum was sometimes called because of King Charles II's patronage of the growing clockmaking industry, improved timekeeping from quarters of hours to within seconds. A seconds hand became the rule, almost, on longcase clocks after 1670. Dials and hands, except for seconds hands, followed the same sequence of design changes on both weight and spring-driven clocks and are considered together in the next chapter.

During the first architectural period of the portico top (Plate 12), it was common to apply a gilded metal ornament, commonly a drapery bunched at each end – a swag – or a festoon of flowers, in the centre. The portico or architectural top was replaced before 1700 by the flat top (Plate 14), which was favoured well into the eighteenth century. It was often decorated by cresting, a wood carving along the front edge, of the hood. On the finest clocks, this was occasionally continued on each side (Plate 13). The domed top (Plate 15) came into favour around 1700, adding appreciably to the overall height of the clock, especially as three metal ornaments were usually mounted on top of the hood. Balls with spires on top, flambeaux (flames) and occasionally figures, such as Mercury, were employed. Towards the end of the first quarter of the eighteenth century square dials were joined by break-arch dials, and later break-arch hoods (Plate 16).

During the last half of the eighteenth century, an unusual shape of top appeared, which had hollow sides as shown in Plate 17, and because of the faintly eastern appearance was called the 'pagoda top', appearing frequently with japanned cases.

From say 1760, makers who preferred plainer styles began to shape the top of the hood to follow the break arch dial. There are odd examples before that date, such as that in Plate 17, but, like all dates for styles, those mentioned suggested the main trend and give a general indication of the period.

In the last quarter of the eighteenth century, the broken arch appeared, in which the curve of the arch is cut out in some way at the top. It became very popular with provincial makers so that, as this was a time of big production, many clocks of the style exist. The swan neck, or horned shape, was also very much in favour at this time for cresting on a flat top, for cheapness. An example can be seen in Plate 20.

In the last period of the longcase clock, over the turn of the nine-teenth century, many hoods were copied from earlier periods, so that the architectural, flat, domed, break arch, pagoda, and varieties of them reappeared, with ornaments, too. This and other features must be studied to avoid making a superficial dating which is too early.

Almost invariably the hood was ostensibly supported by pillars, four in most earlier clocks, the rear ones being quartered in section, but usually two later as the eighteenth century wore on. Some were free-standing, others a part of the hood. At first, they were plain with elaborate gilded metal capitals made up of a number of separate pieces at the top, those at the foot being plainer. Soon the plainer one-piece capital became universal and some makers, cutting costs, made the capital of wood which was gold-leafed. Clocks before 1700 often had Jacobean or spiral pillars – they are also called 'barleysugar pillars' (Plate 15) – but they are rarely seen on clocks after that date, when plain pillars were again in vogue. Fluted Corinthian pillars had some popularity, especially after mid-eighteenth century with pro-vincial makers, when at times, to save cost, only the fronts were fluted.

Longcases gradually grew in height (and width) through the years, from the original six to six and a half feet. After about 1700, plinths, trunks, and hoods, all became wider and the height grew to seven

37

feet or more. During the last quarter of the seventeenth century a few grandmother clocks, only about five and a half feet tall, were made, but these are so rare now as to be well out of the average collector's reach. A few more were made during the last quarter of the eighteenth century also, with, like the earlier ones, 39-inch pendulums.

Doors in trunks were at first rectangular in shape. When the break arch dial and hood came into favour, the top of the door was often similarly shaped, and bevelled or beaded at the edges, too. When provincial makers took the lead in longcase clocks, some of them also introduced, after mid-eighteenth century, doors with wavy edges.

WOODS FOR CASES

Clock cases were made by cabinet-makers and tended to follow furniture styles in woods. The veneer was coming rapidly into vogue when the longcase clock first appeared and the first clock cases were ebony veneered on an oak carcase. At the time, wood was veneered by hand, a very thin slice of the expensive ebony being sawn off and glued to the base wood. The method produced only relatively small pieces, which had to be carefully fitted together and rubbed down to give an even surface and to avoid showing the joins.

Cases were sometimes veneered in pearwood and stained to imitate ebony. Occasionally the early case was of solid oak, but not for the best productions, as oak was the common indigenous wood for furniture, ships, and buildings. Soon after the longcase was introduced, veneers were being used for their other advantage, beautiful figuring. Olive wood became popular for clock case veneering because of its relative hardness and attractive figuring which was ringed and suggested the patterning of oyster shells. The small veneers called 'oyster pieces' have a very beautiful appearance which, once seen, is always recognized again.

Walnut also appeared in veneer towards the end of the seventeenth century and was laid in symmetrical patterns, normally about the centre line of the case. Walnut veneer can be recognized not only by its colour but by its scrolled patterns, known as 'burr walnut' (Plate 13).

The possibility of being able to lay veneers in any direction and having many patterns and colours encouraged casemakers to copy the work of the wood inlayers, and even before 1700 patterned cases were being made. Star-shaped and fan emblems for the corners (*see* Plate 18) were the first and may have originated in the Netherlands. They are made up of alternate triangles of yellow boxwood and black ebony, although at times the ebony was contrasted with hollywood or green-coloured ivory or bone. Designs were soon elaborated into flowers and leaves, and also birds. This design in veneers is called 'marquetry' whether partial or all over the case (Plates 14 and 15). Some of the all-over designs became less representative of Nature, being scrolled patterns known as 'seaweed marquetry'. The marquetry phase ran out early in the eighteenth century and plain veneering returned to vogue.

However, simple fan designs and edging again became popular with provincial makers later in the eighteenth century (Plate 18). This inlaid work is a form of 'parquetry' and was more popular on the continent.

Lacquered cases (Plate 16) came into fashion about the same time as marquetry, but the fashion lasted longer. Most lacquered cases were made in the first half of the eighteenth century. Lacquer furniture first appeared in England in the sixteenth century, and was then called 'Indian' because in Tudor times everything east of Suez was thought to be Indian. The best lacquer work came from Japan and later was called 'japanned work'. The 'japan enamel' of today bears no relation to true japanning, the term having been, like so many others, thoroughly debased. Designs were almost always oriental and raised on the surface. Usually the background was black with designs in blues, greens, scarlets, and yellows. Very occasionally the background itself was red, green, blue, cream, or buff.

Clockmakers used to send parts, particularly doors, of special cases to the East for lacquering, but before the end of the seventeenth century an English japan industry had grown up, as evidenced by a *Treatise of Japanning and Varnishing* published by Stalker and Parker in 1688. In 1701 the industry succeeded in obtaining an Act of Parliament to impose heavy duties on imported work, so after that date until about 1760 most japanning was in fact English, and inferior to the true Eastern work. Most japanned cases have suffered during the years and good ones are valuable. There was a small revival of japanning towards the end of the eighteenth century.

Perhaps the biggest change in woods for clock cases came with the 'new' imported woods of the 1720s, the chief of which was mahogany. By 1750, mahogany had superseded walnut for all high quality work. Mahogany's advantages were its superior strength, straight grain, range of colours, resistance to decay, and relatively quick seasoning. The finest quality was Spanish mahogany, which did not come in fact from Spain but from San Domingo in the West Indies, and being dense and hard was used mostly in the solid. It was followed in popularity by Cuban mahogany, which was similar in colour to Spanish, but not so deeply brown, but was easier to work and especially suitable for veneers because its wavy grain gave attractive figuring. Finally, there was Honduras mahogany from Central America, lighter and softer even than Cuban and often used for the carcase to take a Cuban veneer. Honduras mahogany is also known as 'baywood' and is reddish-brown in colour. It became the most popular wood for better-class longcase clocks and continued in popularity until the end of the longcase period, especially with provincial clockmakers (Plate 18).

Oak was not only employed for constructing the carcases of clock cases but for veneering, for which pollard oak was commonly favoured because of its grain pattern of straight lines of dark dots with wavy light bands crossing them. Often there were inlaid bandings of holly, box, or walnut along the case edges. Solid oak was employed at all times, like solid mahogany, but for 'working' clocks that needed no special decorative appeal and also in large quantities on clocks made for local sale by local clockmakers.

Very cheap clocks, probably made for local farming communities, had softwood cases painted and grained. With simple movements that ran for thirty hours, these were made from about 1750 into the nineteenth century.

Carved oak cases are sometimes encountered. They were usually replacements for other cases which had perhaps become damaged or disliked by the owner during the early nineteenth century. Extreme examples of this kind of case with exaggerated proportions are very occasionally encountered. Carved oaken cases are sometimes called quite wrongly 'Chippendale cases'. The true Chippendale case is rarely seen and was based on designs in Thomas Chippendale's *Gentleman and Cabinet-maker's Director*, a book of designs published in 1754. True, he liked rococo carving, but his clock cases tapered outwards from the foot to the top of the trunk instead of being parallel like almost every English longcase clock. This shape of pedestal for clocks was very much favoured by the French in the eighteenth century, and is neo-classical, after the vogue due to Robert Adam.

Some Yorkshire and Lancashire clockmakers, the country's most prolific during the latter part of the eighteenth century and into the nineteenth, were responsible for what has become known as the 'Yorkshire case'. Usually in mahogany, it was half as wide again as a normal case with a small door in the trunk and an enormous hood covering the painted dial (Plate 20). It was a status symbol for the newly-rich industrialists of the rapidly expanding economy. Another style developed in the north, particularly Lancashire, was the case with a brickwork pattern at the corners of the plinth.

5 Dials and Hands

DIALS and hands of longcase clocks followed a sequence which helps in dating them. The comments here, except for those on the dial sizes and on the seconds hand, apply also to the bracket clocks described on pages 52 to 59.

From the first, longcase clocks had brass dials, square in shape. During the first architectural period of the case, the dial was engraved with the Roman numerals indicating the hours, but almost at once it became common practice to employ a separate chapter ring – a disc of brass with a hole in the middle – which was attached to the dial proper. The central area and the corners were filled by decorative engraving, but again, only a few years after the longcase was introduced, applied ornaments called 'spandrels' were used in the corners and the circular central portion of the dial was matted (Plate 21).

The tradition of the brass dial with separate chapter ring continued right through the longcase period for the best clocks. The chapter ring was silvered, leaving the numerals black, to contrast with the brass background. Occasionally, however, a maker would use a one-piece dial, even for a good clock, silvering it all over. The one-piece dial, like that in Plate 19, but with normal dial markings and hands, came into favour again during the last quarter of the eighteenth century among provincial makers and can always be recognized as it was accompanied by matching hands (page 47). Usually it had a break-arch top.

From about 1780, another one-piece dial appeared, made of iron and painted (Plate 18). It was introduced for cheapness because of the popularity of the longcase clock and was not engraved. Instead, the hours and other indications were painted on a white ground and there were almost invariably coloured decorations of flowers, birds, rural scenes, scenes depicting the seasons, etc. Occasionally a high-grade clock is seen with a painted dial, but most were run-of-the-mill productions for local use. Very, very occasionally a longcase clock is found with a truly enamelled dial, made in the Battersea works.

The dials of the first longcase clocks from 1660 were only about eight inches square to suit the small proportions, and some had engraved bands round the edges. They grew to about ten inches square after the introduction of the long pendulum in about 1675, and to about eleven and twelve inches after 1700. By the end of the eighteenth century some had grown to fourteen inches and even larger. The break arch was introduced towards the end of the first quarter of the eighteenth century and gradually became a more popular shape for better class clocks. Earliest arches were rather flat but soon became semi-circular. Occasionally a square dial modified by riveting on an arch is encountered.

The space in the arch was used for decoration and engraving the maker's name, for a motto such as *Tempus Fugit*, a special indication like the equation of time, an indication for strike silencing, or – after half way through the eighteenth century – commonly for a moon dial, tidal dial, or an animated mechanism; for example, a tossing ship at sea.

The separate chapter ring of the longcase and bracket clock was developed from that first appearing on the lantern clock, which had a single hand turning once in 12 hours. Inside the ring of Roman hour chapters, two concentric circles a short distance apart were engraved and divided into 48 parts to indicate the quarters. Thus time to about half a quarter – $7\frac{1}{2}$ minutes – could be estimated (Plate 9).

This type of dial was used on 30-hour longcase clocks with one hand made throughout the longcase clock period in country districts to meet the need for a cheap timekeeper. They may, because of the dial and hand, be taken wrongly for very old clocks. The cases were very often oak or deal which was painted and grained. Sometimes a minute hand was added at a later date.

It was usual on clocks to engrave IIII instead of IV in order to balance visually the VIII on the other side of the chapter ring. although the tradition of IIII was already well established. The sequence VIII VII VI V IIII looks aesthetically more pleasing than VIII VII VI V IV, it was thought. Occasionally a clock is seen with IV – the Westminster Palace clock, usually called 'Big Ben', is an example.

If a clock is seen with two hands, but a dial marked only in hours with the inner ring showing quarters, it is probably a one-hand clock

43

that has been converted to two. Alternatively, a dial which has one hand only, but is marked with 60 divisions, has had the dial replaced or has been faked.

MINUTE HANDS

The accuracy of the pendulum brought with it the minute hand and a ring of minute divisions, this time outside the chapters (Plate 21). Because of the unfamiliarity at the time of the minute hand, the divisions were engraved in arabic numerals above every hour – 5, 10, 15, 20, 25, etc., up to 60. On the first 8-inch dials, the minutes were engraved between the pair of concentric circles (Plate 21) and occasionally every minute was so engraved.

When the 10-inch dial came into use, the minute numerals were moved outside the ring of scale divisions, but remained fairly small until about 1750 after which they became bigger (Plate 22) – almost as big as the hours on some clocks. Also about mid-eighteenth century a number of makers began to omit the inner ring of quarter-hour divisions (Plate 22). The half-hour decoration between the hour chapters – a fleur-de-lys, diamond, or star, usually – was dropped with the quarters ring, but a few makers continued in the tradition until the end of the century.

Naturally there were some variations of the general trend. One was a wavy minute circle like a series of break arches on some English clocks but more often on Dutch ones, for the Dutch followed the English style of the long case. Provincial makers towards the end of the eighteenth century sometimes favoured a ring of dots to show the minutes, instead of engraved circles. Many painted dials had dots instead of rings.

SECONDS HANDS

When the anchor escapement and long pendulum were introduced, after 1675, the seconds hand became almost universal on longcase clocks because the escape wheel turned once in 60 seconds and it was only necessary to attach a small hand to it. Usually the seconds dial was placed above the centre of the main dial but very occasionally it was below centre, the general layout of the clock escapement having been reversed so that the anchor was below the escape wheel instead of above it.

The style of seconds rings followed those of chapter rings, at first being narrow, then becoming wider. Every fifth second was numbered on the early ones, then just 10, 20, 30, 40, 50, and 60, or on late clocks only 15, 30, 45, and 60. Clocks with $1\frac{1}{4}$ seconds pendulums had escape wheels that made one revolution in 48 seconds instead of 60, so the seconds rings of these are so divided.

SPANDRELS

The corner decorations of dials known as 'spandrels' followed a fairly consistent sequence of development. These were made in brass and gilded and the first ones were always beautifully finished and polished before the gilder carried out his craft. Very soon the finish began to deteriorate until, on the vast majority of clocks in the later eighteenth century, the spandrels were sand cast and gilded without any hand-finishing of the surface. Specialist spandrel casters set up at an early period in clockmaking so that very similar designs are seen on clocks by many different makers. Some makers would favour a particular design and use it until they became tired of it.

The earliest design was the cherub's face with wings on each side (Plate 21). These can be recognized at a glance because they do not fill the corners so much as later designs. By about 1700, the simple cherub's face had become enmeshed in elaborate foliage and scrolling and the wings almost disappeared. Just about this time, a cornerpiece appeared showing two whole cherubs supporting a crown and holding crossed sceptres. Sometimes, in the eighteenth century, a flower was employed as the main symbol of the spandrel, but the face persisted. In some designs, the scrolling foliage was the entire spandrel. One pleasant variation were four different but associated spandrels with figures representing the four seasons, a symbolism also illustrated in the corners of the later painted dials.

HAND DESIGNS

The very earliest hands on longcase, and hanging, clocks showing only the hours were short and stubby with long tails. Some heads had two barbs like an arrow head (Fig. 3). They were a natural development of the hands on earlier types of clock – house clock, table clock, lantern clock – shown in some forms in Fig. 3. The boss

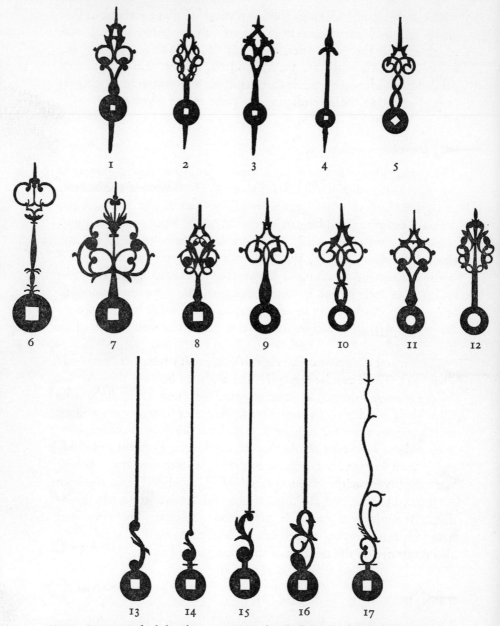

FIG. 3. Longcase clock hands. 1 to 5 Hour hands from one-hand clocks. 6 to 12 Hour hands from two-hand clocks. 13 to 17 minute hands from two-hand clocks. 18 to 22 matching hands. 23 to 27 late forms of matching hands. 23 beetle and poker hands. 24 Breguet, or moon, hands. 27 spade hands. Similar hands were used on bracket and table clocks, and 23 to 27 also on watches.

46

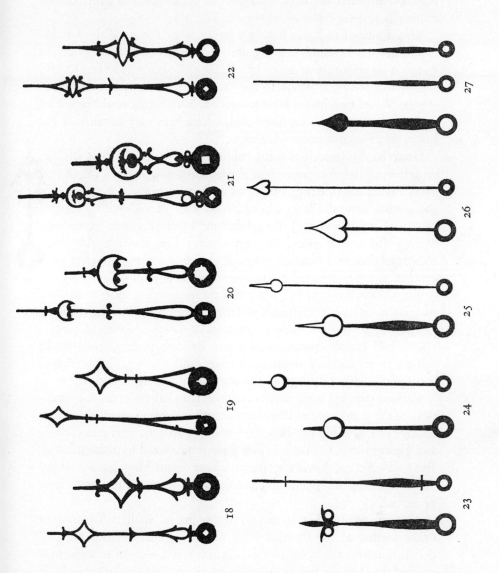

was universally round. The barbs became simple loops to make them more decorative. The decorative part of the hand was at first near the end, and, as the decoration developed, the pierced part became bigger and nearer the boss. Examples of hour hands in approximate chronological sequence are shown in Fig. 3.

The minute hand was hardly known until the pendulum made clocks accurate enough for minutes to be indicated. Makers began to pay a lot more attention to hands. First the hour hand lost its tail, which was provided partly to help to turn it with thumb and fore-finger. When two hands were provided, both hands could be set by turning the tip of the minute hand, which was easy because of the lower gearing and longer leverage.

Hour hands associated with minute hands were at first simple, with the pierced decoration near the tip as shown in Fig. 3 (6). A few years before 1700, designs became almost excessively elaborate. In some cases even the boss was enlarged and pierced with a design. Just after 1700 some of the elaborate hands became excessively narrow for a few years, at least with a few makers. Although elaborate designs remained popular for about three-quarters of a century, simpler designs became more favoured after the firs tquarter of the eighteenth century. One was the cross-over loop which re-mained in fashion for almost as long as the longcase clock (Fig. 3 (9 and 10)). Another very popular design was a series of scrolls, which had certain variations – some delicate with pierced stem; others, from country districts, heavier and thicker. These shapes were particularly common in the last half of the eighteenth century.

Various patterns were more common than others because appren-tices of the more successful clockmakers were often given the rather tedious task of filing out hands from a thin strip of steel and carving and bluing them, the designs being those favoured by their masters. By mid-century, however, there was a flourishing hand-making business in England from which makers could order the pattern they preferred.

At first, minute hands were long pointers, with half-round or other section at the tip and with carved, or carved and pierced, decoration near the boss. The decoration was S-shaped and reminis-cent of the dolphin fret so popular on the fret of the lantern clock. Some are shown in Fig. 3 (13 to 17). Generally, earlier minute hands had smaller pierced loops than later ones and, towards the middle of the eighteenth century, fairly elaborate loops with side-shoots to

48

them were popular. A style introduced about mid-century was the serpentine hand with side-shoots at the curves, also shown in Plate 29.

Despite these variations, some makers continued to use the plainly styled minute hand with a simple S-shaped scroll. There seem to be no particular matchings of hour and minute hand styles, except that hands of matching visual 'weight' were used. A thick, heavy-looking hour hand would have a minute hand of similar appearance.

On the earliest longcase and bracket clocks, up to around 1725, hands would be matched to the dials; that is, the minute hand, particularly, just covered the minute circle on the dial and the hour hand reached just to the inner quarter circle. After hand-making became a separate craft, or perhaps, small batch production had become common in clockmakers' workshops, less care was taken to match the size of the hands to the dial, or the dial to the hands.

MATCHING HANDS

After mid-eighteenth century when the one-piece dial, silvered all over, was introduced by many makers, especially those in the provinces, a new style of hands also appeared. The hour and minute hands were made to match each other, the same design being used for each, except that that for the minute hand was narrower and elongated. The earlier non-matching hands were always made of steel. Matching hands were sometimes made of steel and sometimes of hammered brass. Brass is hammered to harden and toughen it. Examples are given also in Fig. 3 (18 to 22). Matching hands were invariably used with the painted dials with which longcase clocks of cheaper quality were fitted from the end of the eighteenth century into the nineteenth.

One version of matching hands, seen on a few quite early bracket clocks had rounded arrow-head tips and were of brass or steel (Fig. 3 (27)). These eventually became most popular of all, except for longcase clocks on which they were not fitted. Sometimes such an hour hand was used with a minute hand that was a simple pointer. A variation was the pierced arrow head. These arrow-shaped hands are usually called 'spade hands', although the shape is not like a modern spade. Breguet hands, also called 'moon hands', were another variation, the swelled portion at the tip being circular and pierced as shown in Fig. 3 (24). The celebrated watchmaker A. L. Breguet made

D

the fashion popular for his watches but it was employed too by numerous clockmakers in many countries.

Seconds hands were common on longcase clocks with long pendulums, but were very rarely incorporated in bracket clocks. The first type of seconds hand was merely a boss and a plain pointer, a style which persisted well into the first quarter of the eighteenth century (Plates 21 and 22). About this time, hands with tails appeared and thereafter almost invariably they had tails of some sort or another.

CENTRE SECONDS

After about 1740, a longcase clock was occasionally provided with a centre seconds hand. This was a long hand set on the same centre as the hour and minute hands and registering on the minutes scale, like the sweep seconds hand on a modern watch. The centre seconds hand was provided with a substantial tail so that the boss of the hand was at about the centre of gravity (Plate 16). An ordinary long hand being somewhat heavier than a short one, it is inclined to be behind time up one side of the dial and fast down the other, owing to the necessary clearances or backlash in the mechanism. Incidentally, clockmakers have their own time-honoured and literal name for backlash; it is 'shake'.

Hands with counterpoises are commonly used on regulator clocks, made with accuracy as the primary objective, and no doubt originated on them. The regulator, described on page 63, had a special dial, or more accurately three separate dials, as shown in Fig. 4. The hands, or at least the faster-moving ones, were counterpoised to ensure that they registered accurately. Early regulators, like domestic clocks, had separate chapter rings and later ones had all-over silvered dials.

Counterpoised hands are essential on very large clocks with heavy hands. Occasionally on old tower clocks one sees hands with counterpoises which are continuations of the hand. On more modern tower clocks, the counterpoise is behind the dial, out of sight.

There were, of course, many other variations of clock hands too numerous to mention. Some districts had their own peculiarities, some makers their own preferences.

INFLUENCE OF STYLES

The main stream of styling described in the last two chapters refers to English clocks and during the period they influenced continental clockmakers and clockmakers who had emigrated to the new North American states.

A period of development of the French clock industry took place during the time of British clock supremacy and the French gradually caught up and passed the English in decorative clocks. They too had their influence on other countries, so that it is possible to see French 'lines' in some Austrian clocks, and also in Swiss, English, American and others. The American banjo clock is a version of the French lyre clock, and the English balloon (Plate 34) is also French in origin.

6 English Bracket or Table Clocks

THE bracket or table clock,* like the longcase clock, was a result of the invention of the clock pendulum. It was the spring-driven version. Styles ran almost parallel to those of longcase clocks. First cases, from about 1660 to a few years after the turn of the century, were architectural, based on classical buildings, the triangular or portico top being supported (apparently, in the case of clocks) by pillars. Some bracket clocks were like the hoods of the longcase clock shown in Plate 12. An example is the bracket clock in Plate 23.

The first bracket clocks, which are rare and command high prices, had dials which were one-piece engraved all over with a design incorporating tulips which, like the pendulum, were associated with Holland. The Dutch bulb industry was making an impact on the British market at this early date, although the bulbs were very expensive. Tulip engraving also appeared frequently on the back plates of clock movements. The hands were of the early style with simple pierced decoration of the hour hand near its tip.

Perhaps just as early were matted dials with separately attached chapter rings, which were narrow and silvered, or made of silver. The corners were at first engraved, then decorated by application of the simple cherub face spandrels shown in Plate 23. Dials then generally followed the sequence described in chapter five, except that they did not have seconds dials. The same is true of hands.

Cases and movements of bracket clocks became more or less stabilized after 1700 in their general pattern and were produced for half a century or more without much change. Makers in London, who had pioneered production of longcase clocks, turned their attention more and more to bracket clocks, while provincial makers after mid-eighteenth century took over most of the longcase clock

* The term 'bracket clocks' will be used to cover those for standing on tables as well as those for which special wall brackets were made.

production. The reason was, of course, the greater sophistication of the bracket clock for town houses.

It is very unusual to find a spring-driven clock made before the eighteenth century in the provinces. When they were made, they lagged in style, as did longcase clocks, by anything up to a quarter of a century.

Movements, spring-driven through a fusee (see page 101) to make the power output regular, went for eight days at a winding. Some early clocks had alarms, as that in Plate 10a. Almost all bracket clocks struck the hours. Sometimes half-hours were struck by a single blow on another bell of higher pitch. After the end of the seventeenth century, quarter striking became popular. The various elaborations of striking systems and the repeating mechanisms that were fitted to the most expensive bracket clocks so that they could be made to strike at any time by pulling a cord – a valuable feature at a time when artificial lighting was very poor – are described in chapter 12.

Architectural cases, made of ebony veneered on oak, were joined for a few years by cases with Jacobean or spiral pillars and panelled tops carrying gilded metal ornament. These were just like the tops of longcase clocks of similar style at this short period before 1700, as were the architectural bracket clocks.

DOMED TOP

The primary change in case style came with the dome-shaped top with a carrying handle, which appeared after about 1670 and continued right through the bracket clock period of the eighteenth century. A good example is shown in the frontispiece. Domes were shallow at first, well under two inches, but became deeper as the style developed. The dome top, also called the 'bell top', although this is better applied to a later style, was sometimes accompanied by metal finials at the top corners of the case (Plate 25) even to the end of the period, but just as often had none.

The domed top was accompanied by another major change in design, the abandonment of pillars. Instead, the door in front of the dial was plain and stretched the full width of the clock. The glass in it remained square, like its predecessor. There was also a door in the back of the clock, since the hood was not removable like that of the longcase clock. The door at the back was at first of plain wood, but soon was provided with a glass so that the swinging pendulum, and also the decorated back plate of the clock movement, could be seen.

Back plates were engraved to various degrees of elaboration from the last quarter of the seventeenth century for about a hundred years. Early engraving incorporated tulip patterns, like early dials. These were superseded by scroll and acanthus designs (Plate 24), some of which were asymmetrical. In the later eighteenth century, the design on popular productions had become a little more than an engraved border with the maker's name in a central escutcheon (Plate 26).

Early short pendulums were mounted direct on to their arbors and the rear end of the arbor was knife-edge suspension mounted on the back plate. Movement applied to this was often engraved, and sometimes pierced, to decorate it. Some were enlarged very considerably simply to provide extra elaborate decoration (Plate 24). Pierced cocks, equivalent to the pierced cocks that were common on watches, disappeared as soon as the separate spring suspension for the pendulum came into general use, which was much later than it did for longcase clocks.

BASKET TOP

The domed top made of the same wood as the case was accompanied by another version made in lavishly decorated open metalwork, known as the 'basket top', and also surmounted by a carrying handle. Just before the beginning of the eighteenth century, a more elaborate variety with rounded sides, called the 'bell basket top', appeared. Much later, towards the last quarter of the eighteenth century, there was a third elaboration of the metalwork top, the double basket – in fact, a basket top on top of a bell basket top! An example of a basket top can be seen in Plate 27. The case of this is veneered tortoiseshell.

BELL TOP

The bell top in wood appeared towards the end of the first quarter of the eighteenth century. It had a double curve as shown in Plate 28, and was the style copied some fifty years later by longcase makers and called the 'pagoda top' (Plate 17). As well as the simple bell top there was a so-called inverted bell top in which the concave and convex sides are exchanged.

Square glasses and square dials remained in use throughout the period, but were joined before the end of the first quarter of the eighteenth century by the break arch shape (Plate 28). At first this just applied to the shape of the glass in the door and the apparent shape of the dial which was still of brass with corner spandrels. The top of the case remained one of the domed or bell shapes.

BREAK ARCH

The break arch dial rapidly came into fashion, superseding all other styles in the second quarter of the eighteenth century. Often the case top was also of break-arch shape (Plate 30). The semi-circular area of the arch was often used for a 'rise and fall' hand to adjust the length of the pendulum or for strike/silent subsidiary dial, by altering the hand of which the striking mechanism could be silenced (Plate 28). Musical clocks had a tune indicator there and on the very rare occasions when the clock was provided with a seconds dial it would appear in the break arch.

Corner spandrels with cherubs or with women's faces continued almost to the middle of the eighteenth century, but more common after the first quarter were arabesque or foliage designs. These were continued into the arches of break arch dials.

CIRCULAR DIALS

About mid-eighteenth century a few bracket clocks began to appear which appeared to have circular dials, silvered all over, with engraved, black-filled numerals (Plate 29). The glass was round, but it was fitted into a square door covering the front of the clock, the glass itself being mounted by means of a brass ring called a bezel. This eliminated the spandrels. The resultant plainness was continued throughout such clocks. There were no metal decorations on the top or on the door around the keyhole as was common on the traditional bracket clock. The round glasses were at first flat; domed glass appeared later in the century.

From the earliest times side windows were fitted into bracket clock cases so that the movement could be seen and the sound of the bell escaped through a wooden fret above the door (Frontispiece).

Well before 1700, metal became more common for this fret. Then the fret above the door disappeared and sound escaped through the basket top, if this were a feature, or frets were applied to the sides of the case instead of glass. Wooden frets at the side were backed with silk to keep out dirt.

During the last quarter of the eighteenth century, metal fish-scale frets became very common on the sides of ebonized bracket clocks made in embryo factories and sold to clockmakers with the clockmakers' names engraved on them for resale to the public. These clocks usually had round painted dials in break arch cases with matching steel hands and sometimes were repeaters or were musical. The fish-scale frets can be seen in the version shown in Plate 30.

DIALS

Chapter ring development of standard types of bracket clock followed the lines described in the previous chapter. Makers of clocks with circular dials, however, appeared to have reacted against the elaboration. Their one-piece dials had no quarter-hour divisions inside the chapters or half-hour ornaments between the hour numerals. There were, of course, minute divisions in a circle outside the hours. The minutes were engraved in Arabic figures outside this ring at every five minutes. Hands were of steel of the earlier unmatching type or later of brass or steel and matching type.

Later matching dials were painted white with black numerals instead of being silvered, and very few were made with enamelled dials, this being true enamel, i.e. fused glass and not the paint that is euphuistically called 'enamel' today.

Bracket clocks of the traditional shape and size – from about 14 inches to over 30 inches high generally, although there are, still in existence, some very fine small ones by the principal makers – continued to be made after 1800, but there were several other shapes in favour, such as the balloon, which appeared as early as 1760, and the Gothic-shaped lancet.

WOOD TRENDS

Woods of bracket clocks followed furniture trends. The first ones were of ebony veneered on oak and some had applied gilded ornaments each side of the door with perhaps a swag above it to relieve the sombre black architectural case. Not all black wood was ebony. Experts have identified pear-wood, cocus wood, lignum vitae, and others stained black.

Olive wood, introduced before 1700 and employed for longcases was little used for bracket clocks, perhaps because it did not display well on small areas. But it was used in cross-grain strips in conjunction with ebony to give a two-tone finish. The combination was also used on longcases, the 'ebony' sometimes being stained pear-wood, or later on, stained pine.

Few early bracket clocks were veneered with olive wood, most had walnut. Marquetry was applied to some in the early eighteenth century. There were also cases in kingwood veneers and tortoiseshell (Plate 27) applied like veneer. Lacquered cases appeared about the same time as those in tortoiseshell, around 1680, and lacquer remained in fashion to a certain extent until about 1750 in England. Both lacquer and tortoise-shell were popular in the Turkish market in which British clockmakers, particularly Christopher Gould and Markwick Markham, developed a big stake. A painted bracket clock for the Turkish market is shown in Plate 31.

Nevertheless the black case remained most popular of all for spring clocks over a long period despite the phases in woods through which the longcase went.

Turkish market clocks can be instantly recognized by the Turkish numerals. They were made from before 1700 but were most common around the middle of the following century. Many were musical, playing on bells or organ pipes, with a typical hemispherical domed top. Spandrels did not bear women's or cherubs' heads because of the Turkish religious beliefs. There is considerable similarity among the movements of musical clocks of the later eighteenth century for the Turkish market and it seems reasonably certain that they were all made by the same supplier, Thwaites and Reed of Clerkenwell, despite different makers' names on the dials.

PENDULUMS

All bracket clocks with verge and crown wheel escapements (Plate 70) have bob pendulums (Plate 24), the bob being a pear-shaped brass weight on the end of the pendulum rod. The end of the wire was threaded so that the bob could be screwed up and down to alter the rate of the clock. As it was difficult in those times to cut a longish internal thread, a bob had a core of pearwood with a central hole into which the rod was screwed so that it cut its own thread. To adjust the pendulum bob, it was necessary to turn the clock to open the back door, which sometimes disturbed the going when the clock was turned back into position. There was usually a hook on the back plate under which the pendulum rod could be sprung so that the pendulum was held firmly to one side to avoid damage during transportation of the clock.

Many early bracket clocks had mock pendulums to give immediate visual indication that the clock was going. Longcase clocks had their seconds hands, to indicate going, but these were not easy to provide on spring-driven pendulum clocks. The mock pendulum was a small arm with a disc at the end attached to the front end of the verge staff. (The pendulum was at the back end.) This swung to and fro with the pendulum and showed through a curved slot in the dial just above the centre (Frontispiece).

When the anchor escapement was introduced into bracket clocks and the pendulum was suspended from a strip of spring steel instead of being directly attached to an arbor, Thomas Tompion, the most famous maker of the eighteenth century, introduced the flat lenticular-shaped bob (a later version is shown in Plate 26) into his bracket clocks and also introduced an invention which eliminated the nuisance of having to turn the clock and open the rear door in order to adjust the pendulum. His 'rise and fall' mechanism provided a lever on a dial on the front of the clock in one of the corners which could be turned to lengthen or shorten the effective length of the pendulum. One is shown in the Frontispiece. This was done by passing the suspension spring between two blocks fixed to the back plate and raising or lowering the top mounting of the suspension spring.

Another convenience that Tompion fitted to some of his clocks to avoid the need of a door at the back, was a lever on the front, which would cause the pendulum to be held in a fixed position so that the clock could be carried by its handle without damaging the mechanism. Other clocks had a screw fastening on the back plate by which the pendulum could be locked for transit (Plate 26).

Very early spring-driven English clocks just struck the hour; occasionally they struck also the half-hour by a single note on the same or another bell; rarely they sounded the quarters as well. Before 1700, more elaborate systems were developed – Roman striking,

Dutch striking, grande sonnerie, and repeater work. These are described in Chapter 12. Repeating work enabled the owner to make the clock sound the last aural indication at will by pulling a cord with a knob on it from the side of the clock. Fine clocks had a cord at each side so that it could be placed on either side of a bed at night. *See* Frontispiece.

Repeating mechanisms were also provided on clocks *without* ordinary striking work, from an early period down to the nineteenth century. One is shown in Plates 26 and 30.

DIRECTOR'S CLOCKS

When machine-made clocks began rapidly to eliminate hand-workers, special clocks continued to be made in imitation of earlier bracket clock styles, particularly from the last quarter of the nineteenth century to World War I (Plate 32). The uninitiated might date them much too early, but a quick examination will reveal their late provenance by a number of departures from style, Movements are usually fusee with anchor escapement and short pendulum. Often the cases are ebonized. One version fairly often seen is a particularly massive chiming and striking bracket clock, with Westminster and Whittington chimes. Smaller imitation bracket clocks with oak cases are easily recognized for what they are. Because such clocks were often intended for retiring directors they are sometimes known as 'director's clocks'. They have no antiquarian value.

ENGLISH CLOCKMAKERS

The English clockmaking trade was at first centred on London and in the late seventeenth and earlier eighteenth centuries particularly around the Fleet Street area. In the eighteenth century many provincial centres were established particularly around the main towns of Liverpool, Manchester, Bristol, Leeds, Edinburgh, and Birmingham. By the second half of the eighteenth century there were literally thousands of makers scattered all over the country and supply houses began providing them with complete movements.

It is impossible to list all their names. Most will be found among the 36,000 listed in *Watchmakers and Clockmakers of the World* by G. H. Baillie (N.A.G. Press Ltd.) which is in many libraries. Some of the more famous are given in Appendix 3.

59

7 *Other Types of Clocks*

WALL CLOCKS

CLOCKS that hung from the wall with their weights suspended below them were the earliest of all domestic clocks – the iron Gothic clock and the lantern clock. They were followed by hooded wall clocks with wooden cases in England for the first three-quarters of the seventeenth century (Plate 11). These have the general appearance of a bracket clock that is powered by weights.

The first hooded wall clocks were actually lantern clocks with their posted frames enclosed in wooden cases, and wound by pulling on the cords, but later versions had movements with back and front plates which were wound by a key through the dial. Some of them, running for eight days at a winding, were of equal elegance and quality to the architectural longcase and bracket clocks of the time, to which their hoods were closely related.

Although these clocks went out of fashion in England, they retained their popularity on the continent, particularly in Holland, in the Black Forest of Germany, and in Austria. A Dutch version is shown in Plate 68.

After a long gap, the wall clock came into prominence again in England at the beginning of the nineteenth century, but in a different form known as the 'English Dial' because it was in appearance simply a dial with an annular frame or 'case'. One is shown in Plate 33. The case was usually round, but in some examples octagonal, and the movement a spring-driven fusee with short pendulum. The dial was painted white with black Roman numerals and the glass fitted into a heavy brass bezel which was opened to wind the movement or reset the hands. Many English Dial clocks struck the hours. Many were made for government offices and were free from decoration except for occasional reeding of the wood or simple brass inlays.

English Dials continued to be made through the nineteenth century, and into the twentieth, later versions often having a very small trunk below the dial with a door in the bottom through which the pendulum could be adjusted, to avoid taking the clock from the wall. These are not as attractive as the early ones as they stood proud of the wall because of the 'box' at the back, housing the movement. The circular frames of earlier ones were flush with the wall when hung.

Many dial-type clocks were made in the Black Forest area of Southern Germany with wooden movements during the nineteenth century and exported to Britain. One is shown on the right of Plate 65.

REGENCY TABLE AND MANTEL CLOCKS

From about mid-eighteenth century the traditional square brass dialled bracket or table clock was challenged by variations usually plainer in style. One was the round dial, already mentioned (Plate 29), which John Ellicott was an early maker to introduce. The glass for this was still contained in a square door covering the front of the case as with the traditional clock, but before 1800 the circular brass bezel around the glass became the door and had become hinged to the wooden case.

With this change occurred several changes in case design. A popular shape was the balloon shown in Plate 34. This first appeared before the last quarter of the eighteenth century and was probably styled from the French bracket clock of the time, later becoming known as 'balloon' owing to the similarity in shape to the Montgolfier hot air rigid balloons of the late eighteenth century.

Balloon clocks were quite large by modern standards and sometimes provided with wall brackets. Early ones had particularly thin waists. Very often the cases were decorated by veneers, which included a typical radial pattern in an oval shape in the waist, and had metal feet. Although the shape went out of fashion around 1810, it was copied in large numbers later by the manufacturing industry of the Victorian period, such clocks having mass-produced drum movements with cylinder escapements. They were smaller than their predecessors and are normally classified as mantel clocks. A drum movement was in a brass drum for fitting directly into the wooden case.

61

A decade or so before 1800, the arch top came in, being the break-arch with the ledges at each side omitted. The door was just the glass bezel. Soon after, there was a reversion in style to the Gothic shape, but in wood with the lancet top. The Gothic arch was sometimes repeated in the pattern of the frets, if any.

Still another case was called the chamfer top, introduced around 1810. It was a slight stylistic swing towards the architectural period. Clocks of this general style, often with simple but delicate inlay scroll work and square dials and with plain but good quality English fusee movements, were the last of the hand-finished productions and in recent years have been 'discovered' by those who buy and deal in antique furniture and clocks. They are given the embracing name of 'Regency clocks' and the earliest and best fall within the Regency period of 1810 to 1820 when the Prince of Wales (later to become George IV) was Regent to his father George III.

After the Regency period there was great influence from the French Empire style and some English makers copied French clocks with their ormolu (gilded) figures and decorations. These French-looking clocks can be identified by the high position of the winding holes in the enamelled dials. The English fitted fusee movements; the French fitted going barrel movements.

The Victorian period followed from 1837 to 1901 and clock styles generally followed those first developed during the Regency. One cheap type of mantel clock employed a verge watch movement in a small wooden case and became known as a 'cottage clock'. One is shown in Plate 35. The sedan clock was a very similar production (Plate 41).

TAVERN CLOCKS

Before the introduction of the railways when the only means of public transport overland was by means of horse coaches, it was necessary to have some form of public clock at the inns where coaches started and put up overnight. A special type of clock came into use for this purpose and was known as a 'coaching clock' or 'tavern clock'. It was a wall clock with two hands, a seconds pendulum, and a very large dial about two or even three feet across, as shown in Plate 36.

The top of the clock case was round or a typical shape based on the hexagon with two concave sides and one, at the top, of break-arch shape. The shape is sometimes seen today for modern public clocks mounted on brackets from buildings.

The movement was a timepiece, i.e. without strike, driven by a heavy lead weight, usually box-shaped, as opposed to the normal cylinder.

Tavern clocks were often black with gold numerals and painted gold decoration, or the brown varnish colour so often seen in ancient 'pubs'. Sometimes the dial was given an even surface by gluing canvas on the wooden case. Occasionally the case was lacquered, with oriental decoration.

Tavern clocks, made from the early eighteenth century, were in use when Pitt imposed a tax on clocks and watches of five shillings a year and ten shillings for gold watches. Poorer people gave up their timekeepers and kept time by the tavern clock. Apparently inn-keepers began to vie with each other in having the most elaborate and most accurate clocks to draw in people wanting to know the time, but weak enough to stay for a drink. Consequently tavern clocks began to acquire a new name, 'Act of Parliament clocks', although truly an Act of Parliament clock is a tavern clock made during the period of the tax, from 1797 to 1798, during which it reduced the manufacturing trade to half and fell far short of its estimated yield.

A mail coach used to carry its own official timekeeper, which is more truly a watch as it was kept personally by the Mail Guard, who also carried a blunderbuss. The watch was set by a Post Office official at the start of the journey because there was no general time system over the country (Greenwich Mean Time was not adopted until 1880). The coaching clock at the inn was kept in time with the Mail Guard's watch (Plate 37).

THE REGULATOR

After the anchor escapement was invented and the potential accuracy of the longcase clock demonstrated, a demand arose for very accurate clocks. Several clockmakers attempted to improve accuracy by fine workmanship, but a few devoted their inventive powers to the theoretical problems as well, notably George Graham, who in 1715 modified the anchor escapement by altering its geometry so that it did not recoil, so inventing the dead beat escapement (see page 111). The search for accuracy led to the development of a particular type

63

of clock called a 'regulator' in which everything was sacrificed to accuracy.

This type of clock was made from the early eighteenth century right through the nineteenth, long after the normal domestic 'grandfather', for offices, public utilities, and clockmakers themselves for regulating other clocks. Most have now become collectors' pieces but many are still to be found. The first regulators looked just like longcase clocks of the time except for their unusually plain cases, at first of oak and then, when it was imported, of mahogany. These two woods continued in favour, especially mahogany. The clock had a compensated pendulum of some type and in regulators after about 1810 it became the practice to fit a glass door in the mahogany case through which the pendulum could be seen.

Soon the normal brass dial with separate chapter ring was abandoned for a one-piece dial silvered all over and a different lay-out. The dial had three separate hands indicating on three separate chapter rings. The central hand, the longest, showed minutes. Below and within the minutes ring was a small hours ring and above it one for seconds. Often the hours were shown 'digitally' in an aperture, instead of by a hand (Plate 19). The faster moving hands often had tails to counterpoise them so that they did not show a slower time when climbing up the dial than when descending, owing to backlash in the movement (Fig. 4).

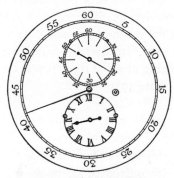

FIG. 4. Regulator dial.

The escapement was usually Graham's deadbeat, although a form of gravity escapement was introduced by a few makers. (See page 114). The pendulum was compensated and a maintaining power, to avoid the clock losing time when being wound, was incorporated

Later movement sometimes had jewelled bearings to reduce friction.

The object of having separate hands was chiefly because of the change of emphasis – the minute and seconds hands were most important. It also eliminited the 12 to 1 gearing known as 'motion work' that enables the minute hand to drive the hour hand concentrically. In a regulator it could be a source of increased friction and potential error.

The seconds hand of a regulator should never be turned backwards because of the danger to the escapement and also because this could distribute the oil wrongly and affect timekeeping. When winding, the cranked key should be given a little pressure in the wrong direction before winding as this will ensure that the maintaining work is correctly engaged.

Not all later regulators have regulator dials; at all times they were also made with orthodox ones. A version popular over the turn of the eighteenth and nineteenth centuries in a mahogany case is shown in Plate 38.

MARINE CHRONOMETERS

At the beginning of the eighteenth century it became apparent that the biggest problem of navigating ships at sea could be solved by having an accurate timekeeper on board. A captain could find his position north or south by measuring the sun's position in the sky and by referring to tables. If it were overhead at noon, for example, he was in the tropics and could find his exact latitude from tables of figures. The difficulty was knowing how far he was east or west. The theory of carrying an accurate timekeeper was that he left port – Bristol, say – with a clock giving him local time in Bristol. At sea he would find noon by using his sextant to observe the sun, and see what time the clock showed. If noon locally were two hours in advance of noon at Bristol, he was 30 degrees west of Bristol, because the earth turns 15 degrees in one hour.

Ships were frequently wrecked and lost through navigational errors in those days. It was easy to make errors of hundreds of miles. In 1741 Commodore Anson spent a month trying to sail round Cape Horn! Although Gemma Frisius suggested using a clock for navigation as early as 1530, it was over two hundred years before it became practicable. The first accurate clocks to be developed were pendulum

E

controlled and it was obviously impossible to make a pendulum go at all, let alone accurately, on a storm-tossed tiny sailing ship.

The problem was solved by using a special small clock known as a marine chronometer. Pioneer of the chronometer was a Yorkshire carpenter named John Harrison whose story, too long to be told here, is one of the world's most inspiring triumphs over every difficulty and opposition. A copy of Harrison's marine timekeeper No. 4, made by Larcum Kendall, was used by Captain Bligh to navigate the *Bounty* and taken by Fletcher Christian, leader of the mutineers, to Pitcairn Island. Both timekeepers are now in the National Maritime Museum at Greenwich.

Pioneers of the practical marine chronometer were John Arnold and Thomas Earnshaw. The timekeeper they evolved towards the end of the eighteenth century – in severe and bitter competition with each other – has continued with little change until today. It was mounted in a brass drum-shaped case itself mounted in gimbals in a wooden box about eight inches square. The gimbals were to allow the chronometer to take up a horizontal position while the sailing ship was heeled over on one tack or the other. A two-day chronometer is shown in Plate 39. Steamships did not become general until mid-nineteenth century and even with them there was plenty of movement that could affect the rate of a chronometer.

The wooden box was of brass-bound mahogany and usually had a brass plate inset in the top on which the navigator or captain had his name engraved, for the chronometer was always his personal possession.

The dial of the chronometer was usually orthodox, but occasionally based on that of the regulator for the same reasons. It was driven by spring barrel and fusee and designed to run for two days or for eight days. Eight-day chronometers were normally for use at base and the others for use at sea. Harrison's maintaining power was incorporated and also an up-and-down dial to show how much the spring was wound. The chronometer was wound by turning it over in its gimbals and inserting a key through a hole in the back after moving aside a dust protector.

The important difference compared with a clock is the chronometer's detent escapement, which interfered least with timekeeping, used in conjunction with a large balance which is temperature compensated and has a helical, instead of a spiral, balance spring. The detent escapement impulses the balance only in one direction, unlike most others, and it swings back in the other direction under the pull of the balance spring. The result is a distinctively slow tick. Pocket watches were also made with detent or chronometer escapements. They can also be recognized by their ticks, compared with most escapements except the duplex, although the outward appearance may be orthodox.

Marine chronometers have long been employed by watchmakers as master timekeepers as an alternative to regulators. In relatively recent years they have also become prized collectors' pieces, because, like the regulator, although functional, they were made in the finest craft traditions, and for that matter, still are by the very few remaining marine chronometer makers.

Here are the names of some of the chronometer makers besides the two pioneers already mentioned: Berthoud, Mudge, J. R. Arnold (son of John), Ditisheim, Cole, Frodsham, Ulrich, Hardy, Schoof, Poole, Dent, Kullberg, Loseby, Mercer, Uhrig, Johannsen, and Usher and Cole. Mercer is the only one still making them, but both Frodsham and Usher and Cole are still in being.

TRAVELLING CLOCKS

In the seventeenth century, special clocks for travelling were already being sold. They remained popular until the day of the railways. In appearance they were almost the same as very large watches, up to about five inches in diameter, which were hung by their pendants from hooks in coaches (Plate 40). The earlier ones were clock-watches, striking the hours, but many eighteenth-century examples were repeaters so that the hours, and sometimes the quarters also, could be made to strike at will. Alarms and calendars were also considered by a number of makers to be essential adjuncts. Travelling clocks were originally provided with outer leather cases to protect them, and often the pendants had a loose joint to enable the watch to hang flat against a surface.

Travelling clocks of the type described were made until about 1800 and for the last fifty years had enamel dials. Sometimes they were set in wooden frames. They were also called 'coach clocks' and 'chaise watches'. A chaise was a light horse-drawn carriage.

During the latter part of the century it was common to fit ordinary verge watch movements into circular frames a few inches across for hanging in coaches (Plate 41). These are usually called 'sedan clocks' today, although at an earlier time their name was 'post-chaise clocks'. A post-chaise was a closed carriage drawn by four horses for fast travelling.

During the eighteenth century many makers supplied small portable clocks, usually to special order, for travelling purposes, and provided them with outer protective cases. They had balance wheels instead of pendulums, of course, and were made in France, Austria and England.

The invention of what is called today a 'carriage clock' can probably be attributed to Breguet, the famous French watchmaker, who devised about 1800 his 'pendule d'officeur', a brass and glass cased travelling clock for officers during the Napoleonic Wars.

After this time a definite form of carriage clock began to emerge, with a rectangular brass (or occasionally wooden) case with glass sides and top panel, and a carrying handle. It was the French who went farthest in development of the 'pendule de voyage' and their separate industry that grew up swamped those of the other nations – from the middle to the end of the nineteenth century. Some French manufacturers continued making carriage clocks into the twentieth century but in much smaller volume. Centres of manufacture were Besançon, the present headquarters of the French horological industry, on the Swiss border, and St Nicholas d'Aliermont, near Dieppe. There were also some makers in Paris.

Movements of French carriage clocks, being visible, were always highly polished and finished, and had platform escapements bridging the top plates. Escapements were cylinder, duplex, and later, lever. Many nineteenth century and early twentieth movements, originally with cylinder escapements, have been converted in present times to lever to bring them into use, because it is very hard to find repairers for cylinder escapements today. Some are timepieces, some strike the hours and half-hours (by a single note) on a spiral rod gong. Some have alarms, with a small alarm dial below the main one (Plate 42). Others are repeaters, including quarter repeaters, and a few even grande sonnerie, striking the full hours after each quarter.

Sizes varied from only three or four inches high to at least a foot, although the intermediate sizes were by far the most popular. Bread-and-butter models were severely plain, special ones often elaborately engraved, enamelled, or decorated with applied rococo or filigree work. Classical and Empire styles with fluted columns were other favourites.

The English made a few carriage clocks, such as that giving mean and sidereal time in Plate 43, and the Austrians were responsible for many of high quality, especially in the early nineteenth century – but it was the French who were the masters of this form of timekeeper in many varieties.

8 Unusual Clocks

GRAVITY CLOCKS

ONE of the first 'novelty' clocks was the rolling clock, also called the inclined plane clock. It is drum-shaped and is placed on a special wedge-shaped stand, down which it slowly rolls, usually over a period of a week. The motive power is gravity.

The clock has a normal movement with verge and balance escapement but the main driving wheel is connected to a lever with a heavy weight on the end of it. The single hand is also connected to this lever. As the drum tries to roll down the slope, it tends to lift the eccentric weight, but is unable to do so. This tends to keep the clock in position on the inclined plane. The slightly raised weight drives the movement, gradually letting the clock roll down as the weight is lowered.

Sometimes the slope was marked with days of the week – a simple calendar. Instead of a hand, there was sometimes a figure apparently balancing on the top and pointing downwards to the dial, which, of course, revolved as the clock descended. In relatively recent times a few rolling clocks have been made in which the dial does not revolve, although the clock itself does, and the hands turn normally.

Probably the earliest novelty clock was also a gravity clock, employing the weight of the clock itself as the motive power. Inside the clock is a drum round which a cord is wound. The clock, usually ball-shaped, is hung from the cord and gradually descends. It was invented in Burgundy in the mid-fifteenth century. Time is shown by a figure pointing to the hour on a moving hand around the waist of the spherical clock case. The clock is wound by lifting it, when the cord will disappear inside, being wound back on to its barrel by a spring. It is called a 'falling ball clock'.

Another form of gravity clock employed a vertical toothed bar, or rack, passing through the centre of the clock. The clock is 'wound' by raising it on the rack. It then slowly descends, the rack teeth driving the clock movement under the power of the clock's own weight. These rack clocks were made as early as 1600 but have appeared as novelties at various times. One that had a run in the early part of the present century was the Silent Keeless clock.

Balls, like large ball-bearings, replaced the direct drive of the main-spring in a few continental clocks of the seventeenth century by Radeloff. The balls ran down a spiral track and, in doing so, rotated a cage to drive the clock. The idea was to use the unvarying force of gravity instead of the variable power of the mainspring to produce a portable but accurate clock.

Jobst Burgi used the mainspring to raise a weight to drive the clock, a system that comes under the generic heading of 'remontoire'. Burgi also modified the verge escapement to operate two bar balances which swung across each other, the object being to increase its accuracy. Several other makers tried this cross-beat system, in-cluding Thomas Tompion, but the most celebrated version was that used in the large marine timekeepers by John Harrison, now in the National Maritime Museum.

Balls were used too, as the *timekeeping* element, instead of a balance or pendulum. Grollier was probably the first to do so in the seven-teenth century, but the best-known version is Congreve's clock, invented in 1808. A small steel ball runs along a zig-zag track cut in a sloping brass table (Plate 44). When it reaches an end, the table is tilted in the opposite direction by the clock and the ball is kept running, first one way then the other. In some clocks, the table is tilted every half-minute and in others every quarter. The time is shown on three dials on an architecturally shaped top. The ball itself indicates seconds as it passes under a series of bridges along the centre of the track. Dents of Pall Mall, London, and Bell of Winchester, still make Congreve clocks.

NIGHT CLOCKS

Night clocks were made from very early times on the continent and came to England in the seventeenth century, probably from Italy, one of the first English makers of them having been Edward East. The dial (Plate 45) had an oil lamp behind it and the time was shown by pierced hour numerals through which the light could shine. The numerals were cut in a disc which revolved behind a semi-circular slot in the dial proper. An illuminated hour numeral took one hour to move through the semi-circle, so its position indicated how much of the hour had elapsed.

Another night timekeeper was the magic lantern clock which was invented in France in the eighteenth century, and was made in the favourite vase shape, as well as others. It projected the image of the dial on to a wall from the back or front of the clock.

MYSTERY CLOCKS

Mystery clocks have been made for over 450 years. The first (probably German, although the French were making them in the nineteenth century) had a circular chapter ring with a hand that travelled around it, driven apparently without any mechanism or connection (Plate 46). In the French clocks the hand was held between two sheets of glass in the middle of the dial. Actually the movement was in the base of the clock stand. The hand was attached to one sheet of glass which was rotated by a shaft drive.

Another mystery clock, invented much later, in 1808 by John Schmidt of London, had a hand in the middle of an open chapter ring and no base in which to hide a movement. This time, the device was even more ingenious. There was a small movement in the counterpoise of the hand which revolved a small weight which altered the balance of the hand, causing it to rotate.

A third mystery clock, invented by A. R. Guilmet of Paris in 1872, is mystifying even after one knows how it works. A figure holds a pendulum and the clock and its dial are quite separate, although on the same base. The pendulum swings to and fro without any apparent motive power and also controls the clock. Actually, the figure is given a slight twist to and fro, but it is so slight as to be almost imperceptible. It is enough, however, to impulse the pendulum and keep it swinging. There are examples in the British Museum and the Victoria and Albert Museum.

Similar in principle and rarer is a clock held aloft by a female figure. Below the clock is hooked a brass tube in a cage of steel rods. At the bottom of the stationary tube is an ornamental brass weight which slowly revolves first in one direction and then the other like the torsion pendulum of a 400-day clock. Actually there is a suspension spring in the brass tube on which the weight twists. The hook is attached to the clock escapement and makes an almost imperceptible movement in the opposite direction at each end of the pendulum's rotation to impulse it.

The most common form of mystery clock was also a figure holding the timepiece, made in large numbers very cheaply from about 1880 onwards. The figure was a woman supporting an oscillating clock on her outstretched hand, or an elephant performing similarly with its trunk. The clock movement and dial form an upper weight on a rod with a pendulum bob at the bottom. This compound pendulum is supported just above its centre of gravity so that it will swing slowly from side to side.

LIGHTHOUSE CLOCKS

The Industrial Revolution in Britain, followed by that in Europe, was a stimulator of novelty clocks that expressed some aspect of mechanization or other changes. One of these was the lighthouse clock, made around the 1880s. It appeared in versions of various complication, the universal feature being that the case was shaped like an early lighthouse, some of which were square in section (Plate 47). The clock dial was in the body of the lighthouse and in some there was a 'lamp' or a rotating cylinder of glass prisms in the top. In others, the clock dial was under a glass dome at the top and turned slowly to face different directions. Most of these clocks were French.

Sometimes the lighthouse clock had a torsion pendulum, in which case the helical spring was seen through the glass 'lighthouse' at the top, as shown in Plate 47.

400-DAY CLOCKS

The torsion pendulum is one that rotates slowly first in one direction and then the other, instead of swinging fairly rapidly to and fro. Because of its slow period of oscillation, the torsion pendulum will run for a long time at one winding of the clock spring – usually a year or longer. Such clocks are still made in large numbers. The pendulum, a flat heavy disc at the bottom of the clock, is visible, as the whole clock is placed under a glass dome.

These '400-day' clocks are usually German. They were first made

73

some time before 1880 and the earliest had a rectangular plate move-ment of normal appearance mounted on pillars, underneath which was suspended the torsion pendulum, a more elaborate arrangement than that on modern productions, as shown in Plate 48. Some employed a ball hung from rods which at first sight was more like a normal pendulum. Next in chronology came a pendulum com-prised of four balls on arms, the idea being temperature compensa-tion, as a mechanical linkage made the balls move inwards slightly as they expanded outwards in heat. This first appeared before 1900, and set the pattern as four-ball pendulums became, within two years, the most common, although they were fixed, and attempts to compensate for temperature forgotten.

In the USA, early 400-day clocks, also called 'anniversary clocks', have some antiquarian value; in the UK they have little, if any.

STEAM-ENGINE CLOCKS

The steam-engine clock was particularly expressive of the Industrial Revolution, which depended upon power. This had a model of a steam engine on top with working pistons and governor. Another version was the beam engine, in which the beam is actually the balance which controls the timekeeping of the clock (Plate 49).

Also popular at the same time was the ship's captain clock. The pendulum operated a model of a man at the wheel of a ship who rocked to and fro, 'holding the head into wind'.

There was considerable revival of automata clocks from about the last quarter of the nineteenth century and into the early twentieth. Automata clocks were among the first productions of the Augsburg in the late sixteenth century, but they were revived in both France and Germany in different ways. The Black Forest clockmakers' work, including their automata, is described separately on pages 84 to 86.

PICTURE-FRAME CLOCKS

About the end of the eighteenth century, the picture-frame clock came into fashion in France. A real gilt picture frame was used with a background of green, blue, or red velvet in which the clock dial was set, sometimes with brass spandrels. A more elaborate variation, also made in the Black Forest of Germany, was to have a painting with a church clock tower in it, the dial of which was a true clock. Automata also commonly appeared in the picture, a favourite being a windmill with turning sails, and two men sawing a tree trunk, a blacksmith at a forge, trains and sailing ships. These appeared particularly in the period 1850 to 1870. The figures were usually made of cardboard, although occasionally of iron, and sometimes a musical box was incorporated.

None of the pictures was three-dimensional, but 3-D scenes were sometimes made, a ship tossing on a stormy sea being typical. The scene was covered by a glass shade.

TICKET CLOCKS

The early twentieth century was a time also when people were becoming ticket-minded because of the new ticket-issuing machines. One result of this was the ticket clock, which showed the time in figures on small cards, 'digitally' as it would be described today. The 'Plato clock', to give it the inventor's name, was patented in 1902 by an American, E. L. Fitch. The first ones appeared in 1905 in rectangular and cylindrical glass-sided cases similar to those of French carriage clocks. These were made in the USA. Then, just before the First World War, the French and Germans started making them (Plate 50). Quite recently a German version has reappeared.

FLYING BALL CLOCKS

A German version of a French nineteenth-century clock currently made for an American company may also deceive the unwary into thinking it original. This is the flying ball clock. On top of the small wooden case is a T-shaped arm with a thread and ball attached to the end of one arm. The T turns, and at each half-turn, the ball flies out and causes the thread to wind round a rod, then unwind to free itself. Originals are not often seen. They were invented in 1883 by P. Closon, and some had a model of a cherub with an umbrella, or a fisherman, instead of the T arm.

ELECTRIC CLOCKS

In the second quarter of the nineteenth century, many scientists and inventors were turning their talents to new uses for 'galvanism', which was then little understood. Among them was Sir Charles Wheatstone, who devised an electric clock, but the first practical system was thought of and constructed by Alexander Bain, a clockmaker who had made a printing telegraph apparatus and also first suggested the idea of an electric clock to Wheatstone. A few of Bain's clocks are still about in private hands. They look at first sight like normal 'grandfather' clocks. Others are in shorter cases, and quickly recognized. The long pendulum is impulsed by electromagnetism. The bob is a magnet attracted to one side then the other by fixed coils of wire through which a current passes. The pendulum rod moves a slide which changes over the current. The current came from a quantity of coke buried in the ground with several zinc plates buried a few feet away, each connected by copper wire to the clock. The coke and zinc were kept watered and formed an elementary electric cell! More usual were rods in the ground, one of copper and the other zinc. There are no weights, as the clock is driven from the pendulum (Plate 51).

Another successful maker of electric clocks at this early period of electricity was C. Shepherd. One of his clocks is still working in the wall of Greenwich Observatory and another was rediscovered in 1965 in Deal, with parts of a time ball that it once operated. The time ball fell down a mast at a predetermined time so that masters of ships could set their chronometers by it.

The Bulle clock (not to be confused with Buhl or Boulle, a form of inlay with tortoiseshell or ivory) was an electric mantel clock with a short pendulum employing a system similar to Bain's. It was made in France from early in the twentieth century. One is shown in Plate 52. The brass cylinder or pillar holding the movement was once the container for a Leclanché cell, but a small $1\frac{1}{2}$-volt dry cell can now be used to run such a clock for a long time. There are probably plenty of Bulle clocks still to be found and they have now even reached antique shop status.

The Eureka clock is very different in appearance. It employs a very large balance wheel instead of a pendulum. This balance which completely dominates the clock movement is driven by an electromagnetic system (Plate 53). The clock was invented in 1906. Versions are still commonly made by amateur mechanics.

Anyone interested in early electric clocks should see the collection in the time gallery of the Science Museum in South Kensington, West London.

A number of early electric clocks had a device called a Hipp toggle, and are sometimes called Hipp clocks, although they may have been made by someone else. In 1842, Hipp, a Swiss clockmaker, had the idea of causing a little toggle on the pendulum rod to brush backwards and forwards over a notch on the top of two open electric contacts. When the pendulum arc began to fall off, the toggle caught in the notch and forced the contacts together momentarily, which completed a circuit to impulse the pendulum.

Most Hipp clocks were made by the Telegraph Manufacturing Co., of Neuchâtel, and had half-second pendulums. Some Hipp toggles had a wire attached with a paper or mica vane on the end to brake the toggle so that it lagged behind the swing of the pendulum. These are sometimes called 'butterfly escapements', a term which is also rather inappropriately applied to the ordinary toggle.

INDUSTRIAL CLOCKS

John Whitehurst, F.R.S., of Derby, a highly ingenious clockmaker, invented an industrial clock in the later eighteenth century which was made in some numbers and is now a collector's piece. Its purpose was to keep check on night watchmen and it is known as a 'tell-tale' clock. The clocks were in narrow or tapering long cases made of oak and had 12- or 24-hour dials which rotated. Around the dial was a series of protruding pegs. When a night watchman visited the place where the clock was situated he pulled a plunger which depressed the peg at the time of his visit on the dial. The clock later returned all pegs to the cocked position. A German version of a night watchman's clock is shown in Plate 65.

SKELETON CLOCKS

The Victorians loved skeleton clocks in which the plates were reduced to a minimum by cutting them away until nothing but decorative frets remained, as shown in Plate 54. They stood on wooden or marble bases under glass domes.

The style probably came from France where several celebrated makers had devised them in more elegant form, from about 1750, with bases of marble and often sunray pendulums and pin-wheel escapements. The most typical feature of French skeleton clocks made later – over the last quarter of the nineteenth century and first quarter of the twentieth – was a very large main wheel, similar to that which can be seen in Plate 56.

At the Great Exhibition of 1851 in London, a miniature French skeleton clock with a movement only 6½ inches high was on show. It sold in great numbers and there is still a number to be found. The base is of wood and conceals an alarm bell, which is of hand-bell shape and is wound and set by pulling two cords, which avoided removing the glass dome (Plate 55).

English skeleton clocks are often massive, and include timepieces, strikes, chimes, and even musical versions. Several are known that run for a year at a winding. They were made from about 1840 and almost invariably had fusee movements. Shapes were often of Gothic origin. 'Reproductions' of famous buildings were another vogue (Plate 54).

Anchor escapements with short pendulums were normal for 'skeletons', but after 1880 many were made with detent escapements to provide dead beat seconds, the short half-seconds pendulum causing the seconds hand to move only at every other swing. After about 1870 some had large platform escapements with lever escapement and balance wheels instead of pendulums (Plate 56). There were even a few electric skeleton clocks.

Manufacture in quantity more or less finished in England in the first quarter of the twentieth century, but there is still a clockmaking firm in existence, Haydock of Ashbourne, Derbyshire, that has original patterns, castings and designs.

WATER CLOCKS

There are about the country many clocks driven by a flow of water from a tank into a float chamber, the rising float causing the hand to turn. These are made of lead or brass and wood and often bear a date such as 1646. The lead ones have markings which have led some 'experts' into thinking them genuine. They have at times fetched good prices in auctions. In fact all were originally made as novelties, and not even sold as reproductions. There is no such thing as a genuine water clock of the type. One is shown in Plate 57.

Some are genuine water clocks, or clepsydra, of course. The earliest were Egyptian, Roman, or Greek. In the seventeenth and eighteenth centuries, a 'falling drum' water clock was made. The drum contained fixed vanes with small holes in them and was partly filled with water. It was suspended from a cord wound round each end of a fixed axle through the drum and descended slowly as the water leaked through the holes in the vanes to the lowest part of the drum. The time was indicated by the rotating drum against a pointer that did not rotate. A version of this clock was marketed very recently – in 1964. It is actually a gravity clock (like the falling ball clock described on page 70), except that it is controlled by water.

9 Foreign Clocks

To MOST people, a typical French clock is now well known enough to be easily identified, as it has a round dial in an ormolu case, which often incorporates draped figures and has elaborate ornamentation. There is considerable confusion about the word 'ormolu'. Literally it means 'or moulu' or ground gold and refers to the fire or mercuric gilding with which the cases were finished. The gilding process is dangerous to health and has now been supplanted by electro-plating. Ormolu was often left matt on some part of the clock case and polished by burnishing on others.

Most of the French clocks of this type seen around the antique shops are reproductions of old clocks made by casting them in a zinc-based alloy, or spelter, from patterns, and electro-gilding them, during what is called the Second Empire period of Napoleon II, from 1852 to 1870. (It was also the time when many ingenious French novelty clocks were made.) By comparing an original ormolu clock with a reproduction, it is possible to see the much more meticulous finish of the earlier period against the less sharp copy and less careful casting of the metal.

The earliest French clocks, like small towers, were referred to in Chapter 1. France became the most powerful country in Europe during the reign of Louis XIV, from 1643 to 1715, which attracted to the court many French and foreign artists (in the true sense of the word, not just the narrow one of 'painters', now fashionable), who greatly encouraged clockmaking.

In the later seventeenth century, cases were of wood, at first ebony then white wood, particularly poplar, elaborately ornamented with acanthus leaves and draperies. Some were made to stand on wall brackets like the English bracket clock, but the brackets were as ornate as the clocks. Others were intended for small tables or had specially made ornate stands on the floor. Most of these clocks appeared after the invention of the pendulum in 1657 and had a crown wheel and verge escapement with short pendulum. Suspension of the pendulum was by a silk thread and not by rigid attachment to the verge arbor like English clocks.

Boulle (or Buhl) inlay work first appeared during the Louis XIV period, employing tortoiseshell, instead of wood veneers, combined with brass or pewter and ivory.

Towards the end of Louis XIV's reign, a style called 'religieuse' was introduced, reacting against the flamboyance of the earlier cases, although it was still decorative compared with contemporary English productions. The cases were mostly rectangular and of ebony veneered on oak with an arched or bell top. The front was supposed to represent the façade of a palace; in fact the style appears to have been influenced by the English bracket clock of the time, with its corner pillars. Below the dial was an applied ormolu decoration, representing Father Time, draped figures, leaf decoration, etc.

Many clocks of this period had the chapters in enamel instead of being engraved on an annular-shaped chapter ring. Owing to the difficulty of enamelling larger pieces of metal, each chapter was separate, and usually shaped rather like a shield, these twelve enamelled chapters being set in a metal dial. Occasionally, five-minute mark chapters were included also. Enamelling means using true enamel, powdered glass fused in a furnace on to a metal base. Such dials were used principally with Boulle work.

The twelve enamelled chapters were separate cartouches. On better clocks a thirteen-piece enamel dial appeared with an enamel centre as well as the twelve chapters. These all met at the edges to give the appearance of a whole dial made of enamelled sections. Today the feature always puts up the price.

The next period was Regency (1715 to 1723) when there was little development in new clock styles except that the balloon shape, later to appear in English clocks, came quickly into favour. The clock was usually on a wall bracket. (This shape was adopted by the Swiss and is still a favourite there today, where it is called 'Neuchateloise', but is more waisted than balloon in shape.)

In Louis XV's reign, the longcase clock continued from the earlier period. This was extremely ornate with curvaceous sides, appearing more like a small clock on an elaborate stand than one with a long pendulum. The typical French balloon type bracket clock was very popular, in carved wood and in marquetry and bronze.

The cartel clock also appeared. This was a wall clock with elaborately carved wooden case, or a similar one cast in bronze. The wooden ones were decorated in many cases by a process known as 'vernis Martin,' in which drawings of flowers were coloured and varnished. In cheaper versions the pictures were printed. The most important trend was the increasing use of bronze for cases.

Greatest French period for clocks was that of Louis XVI, from 1750 to 1790, when the output of an astonishing variety of ornamental and technically important clocks was prodigious (Plate 58). Some very fine regulators in long cases with glass doors were made by clockmakers of the calibre of Berthoud. The cases were straight-sided, and with more restrained decoration than most other French clocks, although there was often an elaborate bronze decoration on top. Pendulums were almost always Harrison gridiron. Dials had concentric hands, unlike most English regulators, and sometimes there was a centre seconds hand (Plate 59).

Domestic clocks were made of ormolu, of marble, and of both. Wood was less frequently a material. Draped or undraped classical figures were a favourite ornament, and also cherubs, always modelled in full relief. The variety of design was immense. Often the clock was supported on pillars between which hung the pendulum bob representing a rayed sun. Lyre shapes appeared and there was Egyptian influence in a number of designs after Napoleon's Egyptian campaigns.

The urn or vase shape was popular for its novelty when the time was shown by moving bands of numerals for minutes and hours. Often the clock had a figure holding a ball round which the hour band turned. This was a revival of an old Augsburg idea. Cartel clocks were also produced in big numbers.

Some of the more important clocks had calendar dials, including annual calendars, and moon dials. Concentric hands for the various indications were more frequent than in English clocks. The dials, too, were of enamel, as craftsmen had mastered manufacture of these in larger sizes.

During the following very short period of the Revolution (1789 to 1799) there was an attempt to introduce decimal clocks, a few of which are still in existence. The dials were divided into five or ten sectors instead of twelve or twenty-four. There was an attempt, too, to revise the months into periods of thirty days with new names and a few clocks were made with these calendars.

About this time, picture-frame clocks with elaborate animated scenes appeared. These were copied in cheaper materials at a later period by the Black Forest industry.

In the Empire period of 1799 to 1815 that followed, ormolu clocks continued to appear in many styles, including vases, lyres, and Roman chariots. Ornaments were much influenced by classical Greek and ancient Egyptian motifs. Many clocks supported on columns were made, often with short gridiron pendulums hanging in the centre of the columns. Regulators were numerous and some magnificent complicated clocks and astronomical movements and spheres were devised by the finest makers, including Janvier, and Raingo. Breguet, the famous watchmaker, also produced elaborate small clocks of supreme excellence.

From about 1830 to 1836 there was a minor revival of the Gothic style in France and some clock cases were inspired by Gothic cathedrals. This was also a time, around 1830, when the three-dimensional animated scene appeared, one version showed a light-house with a clock in it near a ship tossing on the waves under a glass dome. They were made until about 1860, by which time the quality deteriorated. Picture-frame animated clocks were still being produced, and various other automata clocks. One novelty of later in the century was the flying ball, and another the skeleton clock, both described in Chapter 8.

France, being a relatively large country, had groups of regional clockmakers who developed their own identifiable styles, particularly noticeable in longcase clocks, which were much less elaborate than Parisian productions. Cases were often straight or tapering out towards the top. The violin shape was common, too. In the Comtois, an easily recognizable movement was turned out in large numbers. It was primitive, having a frame of iron bars like the old lantern clock, but with an inverted verge, the crown wheel teeth pointing downwards. There was rack striking, the rack being straight and vertical. A peculiarity of the striking is that the hour is struck and then repeated two minutes later. Half-hours are also sounded.

Comtois clocks are found in long cases of white wood 'grained' by painting. The cases are violin-shaped at the sides and the pendulum is a large violin-shaped object of embossed sheet iron, elaborately coloured, as shown in Plate 60. It is made in halves, the lower half of which can be raised or lowered for regulation of timekeeping.

French carriage clocks are described in Chapter 7.

BLACK FOREST CLOCKS

Even today, an antique dealer will occasionally offer a 'Dutch clock' in which case, dial and movement are all made of wood. Sometimes there are carved animated figures, too. These clocks were actually made in the Black Forest area of south Germany and were called 'Deutsch' clocks. Wooden clocks were never made in Holland, but the misnomer has persisted for centuries.

The Black Forest clock industry started towards the end of the seventeenth century among farmers skilled in wood-carving, who supplemented their meagre incomes by home crafts. The plates of the movement were of wood, as were the toothed wheels (Plate 61). 'Lantern' pinions were made by a series of pins between two wooden discs like a squirrel cage. The escapement was a verge and foliot; a wooden wheel with pins parallel to the edge was the farmer's version of the crown wheel.

The pendulum was generally introduced probably after the first quarter of the eighteenth century. A short pendulum was at first hung *in front* of the dial and worked with the same type of verge escapement. Locally the pendulum was known as a 'cow's tail', the name by which the clocks are sometimes called (see Plate 65). The case was a simple wooden box with a painted dial on front. It was common to have an upper hand indicating hours and a lower one quarter-hours, which avoided extra motion work gearing. Usually flowers were painted on for decoration. Striking came in about the same time and early bells were of glass, that also being a Black Forest trade, but were very soon supplanted by metal ones.

About 1750, the anchor escapement was introduced, with a brass escape wheel. The anchor was a simple bent strip of steel and the pendulum, with its lightweight bob, was moved to the back of the clock, being hung from the pendulum rod by a small hook on a long rod from the bob. About the same time, clockmakers began using brass wheels, but still with wooden arbors and plates. Also, normal hour and minute hands became the rule.

The dials were separate from and bigger than the wooden box case. Often they had arched tops (Plate 65). The clock itself was usually hung on the wall with the weights hanging from chains below. The first ones were painted in water-colours, then oil was used. At an early date, many had the dial and decoration hand-printed on paper glued to the dial plate. In the last quarter of the eighteenth century, dials were treated with a mixture of whiting and varnish which yellows with time, and is an indication of the clock's age, since later ones do not yellow so much.

A novelty introduced about mid-eighteenth century was the shield clock, made on the same principle, but with a shield-shaped dial. This was at times used for a trophy and often ornamentally carved. The shape was derived from the plate clock or 'Telleuhr' made originally in Augsburg (Plate 63) with a flat metal dial and elaborately shaped edges with repoussé decoration. Dials were often of pewter or silver and a cow's tail pendulum hung in front.

The names which may be found on the front of a Black Forest clock are sometimes those of a bride and groom and the date that on which they were married and given the clock as a present.

Picture-frame clocks were referred to in an earlier section. They were made with painted pictures on a metal plate incorporating a clock. Another novelty was the station house clock, the style of its case being based on a railway station building with a gabled roof.

The clock which became most famous was the cuckoo clock, first made by Franz Ketterer about 1740. Most cuckoo clocks encountered today are recent productions, but still all made in the Black Forest of Germany, despite the common delusion that they come from Switzerland. The cuckoo sounds the quarters.

The first cuckoo clock had shield dials with a door in the arch through which the cuckoo appeared to make its call before the hour only, which was struck on a bell (Plate 62). The dial gradually changed to the distinctive cottage carving (Plate 64). The wooden plate for the movement continued until nearly the end of the nineteenth century. Very occasionally, a quail to sound the hours by its own call was added to the cuckoo (Plate 64).

Black Forest makers used to hawk their own clocks by carrying them around in packs. There are some novelty clocks about showing the clockmaker himself on his rounds.

Automata other than cuckoos were added to clocks by the Black Forest makers, particularly during the score or so years after 1850. Often these were little men striking the bell in the arch of the clock.

Occasionally these hanging clocks are seen today mounted by some later owner in a long case.

Black Forest makers also applied their ingenuity to musical clocks, adding musical barrels with combs to play tunes at the quarters and hours. They employed bellows, made, incidentally, of chicken skin, such as those used for the cuckoo to produce organ clocks which played tunes. A special type was the 'trumpeter clock', which first appeared in 1858 and was later combined with a musical box.

The industry also made more orthodox dial clocks such as 'drop dial' clocks. These had cases of figured wood with simple brass inlay decoration, white painted dials, and wooden plate movements with short pendulum and hour strike. Reverting to an early practice on lantern clocks, they had tiny 'spurs', i.e. pins, at the bottom back of the clock to dig in the wall and prevent accidental movement.

In the last quarter of the nineteenth century Black Forest makers turned out huge numbers of what are called 'postman's alarms'. The painted dial with movement behind it hung on the wall with weights and pendulum hanging below. Some had glasses and some not. There was an alarm, with a bell, or two bells on top of the case.

AUSTRIAN CLOCKS

Austrian clocks followed in general the leading styles of the time. Before the invention of the pendulum clock, they were identified with the south German, French, and Italian trends; afterwards with the English, and in the early nineteenth century with the French. There are differences which will identify many of them on sight. The Austrian longcase clock of the eighteenth century usually had a brass dial similar to English productions, with silvered chapter ring, but the case had a curvaceous outline more reminiscent of the French taste, but without the applied decoration. Bracket clocks were much more like the English ones, although sometimes with a little more decoration, until about mid-eighteenth century when the French influence became more pronounced.

About the same time a clock appeared that was a truly Austrian style. Called a 'Stockuhr', or sometimes a 'Stutzuhr', it was a fairly large mantel clock with a pillared base, usually having a mirror behind the pillars to reflect them and the sun pendulum. The dial was skeletonized in the best examples, with animated figures, as shown in Plate 66.

Some of the finest Austrian clocks were made after 1800, many after French ormolu styles and many carriage clocks. One style, typically from Vienna, was called a 'Laterndeuhr', or lantern clock, although it was nothing like the English lantern clock of an earlier period. It was four feet or more long in a wooden framed case with glass front and sides, and hung on the wall. The dial was behind the glass door and there was a seconds pendulum with a heavy brass-covered bob. A particularly fine example is shown in Plate 67. It runs for a month at a winding and has a true enamel dial with ormolu rosettes around it.

Later, these clocks became known as 'Vienna regulators', because the first ones were very accurate and dry pine pendulum rods in the best gave some measure of temperature compensation. However, the style became very popular and in the second half of the nineteenth century they were turned out industrially in large numbers. The cases and pendulums became shorter; the cases were made of inferior materials, the pendulum bobs became light in weight, and, strangely, the seconds hands went round the 60 seconds dial in a period of much less than a minute.

An unusual clock only about $2\frac{1}{2}$ inches high was made in Austria not long after 1800 with two fast swinging pendulums in front of the dial, or sometimes just one. This is called a 'Zappler'.

DUTCH CLOCKS

The Dutch made many watches as well as clocks, particularly through the eighteenth century. Although a Dutchman, Christiaan Huygens, invented the pendulum clock, it was developed by the English and the Dutch tended to follow English styles, particularly in longcase clocks, although Dutch ones can often be recognized by a bulbous base to the case.

Typical of early eighteenth-century Dutch clocks is the Zaandam style, which is a form of lantern clock standing on a wall bracket with weights hanging below. The posted movement had a verge escapement, and short pendulum separately mounted on the case. This developed into the more ornate Friesland clock (also called a 'stoeltjesklok') because it stood on a little platform, or stool, on a wall bracket. The bracket had an ornate hood and there were cast lead or pierced wood decorations around the clock as shown in Plate 68.

The staartklok, appearing around 1750, also came from Friesland.

The movement was of primitive posted style, like a lantern clock, with anchor escapement and seconds pendulum. The pendulum hung in the narrow case and could just be seen through a glass near the bottom covered by some ornamental metalwork. Weights hung in front of the case. The painted dial was enclosed by a sliding hood like that of a longcase clock, but without a glass. The whole clock hung on the wall. A plain version is shown in Plate 69. The dials were frequently repainted to keep them fresh, unlike those of most other nation's clocks.

Clocks with wooden dials and movements are often called 'Dutch clocks', although all came from the Black Forest of Germany. (See page 84.) Dutch clocks had a peculiar system of striking, described on page 125.

SCANDINAVIAN CLOCKS

The Swedes, Norwegians, and Danes made clocks at early periods. Some of the finest of the late sixteenth and early seventeenth century were made in Denmark by Jobst Burgi working for the astronomers Tycho Brahe and Kepler. Many were astronomical globe clocks.

In the eighteenth century, the Danes made a clock very much like the English longcase, but known as a 'Bornholmer clock' after the island where it originated.

AMERICAN CLOCKS

In the eighteenth century, the American clockmakers were mostly colonists from Europe and particularly England, so the English style in longcase clocks prevailed. Developments followed the general pattern described earlier in this book, with a few variations, such as the 'whale's tails' decoration on clocks with break-arch hoods, that appeared around 1790. The curved top had attached to the front edge a cut-out of scroll shapes, like those in Plate 16.

Owing to the shortage of metal, many movements of 30-hour longcase clocks were made with oak plates and wooden wheels, except for a brass escape wheel. Other types of clock were made later with wooden movements, this time for early experiments in mass production, by Eli Terry, Seth Thomas, and Silas Hoadley. When metal became more easily available, around mid-nineteenth century, clocks were made in brass.

Eli Terry specialized in wooden shelf clocks, a design peculiar to America, which was made in large numbers from 1820. The clock was about two feet tall and of thin rectangular shape with a large square painted wood dial. The door was glazed, but the lower portion, not so high as that covering the dial, was painted with decorations or a scene, a hole being left in the middle for the pendulum to be seen. The clock stood on pointed feet with a scroll cut-out in front between them. There was cresting on top similar to the horned cresting on English longcase clocks. It was weight driven. (Fig. 5.)

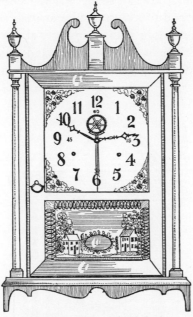

FIG. 5. American shelf clock.

This type of clock was probably introduced by the Willard family, who were also responsible for another domestic shape, the banjo clock with a round top and a rectangular base. It was produced from 1802 to about 1860 and was pendulum-controlled and spring-driven. A similar but less angular form was the acorn, or hour-glass, clock, no doubt inspired by the French lyre clock of an earlier period. This, however, stood on a wall bracket instead of hanging on the wall.

Shortage of materials, in this case spring steel, was responsible for the appearance of a strange clock about 1818. The inventor, Joseph Ives, fitted a waggon spring in the base of the clock to drive the movement. A waggon spring clock is shown in Plate 71.

89

In the later nineteenth century, Seth Thomas made large numbers of rectangular-shaped wall clocks which were similar in general appearance to Terry's shelf clocks with a glass door panel at the bottom portion which was divided from the top by a cross bar. These were pendulum-controlled and weight-driven and the movements were good early examples of the ingenuity of the man who is now called the 'production engineer' as bent wires replaced the forged, filed, and polished steel parts of hand-made clocks, a system pioneered in the Black Forest of Germany.

One other typical American shape was the steeple clock, a shelf clock with a ∧-shaped top with a spire at each side (Fig. 6). The entire front was a glass door shaped similarly at the top and with the bottom glass separated by a cross-piece and painted with some decoration. Its shape was a variation of the Gothic theme.

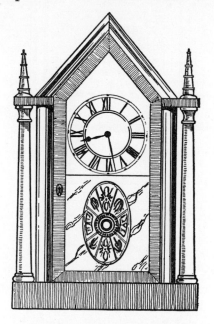

FIG. 6. American steeple clock.

Perhaps one more American clock should be mentioned as it was thought by the uninformed public to have been made at the date stated on the case, 1492. Known as the 'Columbus clock', it was, in fact, made in 1892 (almost entirely of wood) in the Black Forest of Germany to imitate a fifteenth-century clock and was marketed in the USA to celebrate the 400th anniversary of the landing of

Columbus. Later it was mass produced in the USA. Columbus clocks were actually slightly modified versions for selling purposes of stocks of another novelty clock which bore the fictitious date of 1640 and was called the 'Mozart clock'.

10 Clock Mechanisms

THE technical history of clocks falls into two broad categories. One is the never-ending quest for greater accuracy of timekeeping, and the other is in attempts to provide and develop ancillary indications – moon dials, chimes and music, planetary indications, tidal dials, and so on – what might be called 'gadgetry'.

Taking the search for better timekeeping first, the escapement that made the mechanical clock possible is called the 'verge' It is an arbor to which are attached two small plates – the pallets – like flags on a flag-pole. The name probably comes from the Latin *verga*, a wand, which also gave us 'verger', who leads a church procession with a wand of office. The verge works in conjunction with a band wheel which has sharp teeth cut in one side and is called a 'crown wheel' because of its likeness to a royal crown, as shown in Fig. 7.

The verge escapement was an essential part of clocks for nearly four hundred years, and lasted nearly five hundred years in watches; it is therefore of considerable importance to collectors, who should be able to recognize it and understand its function. This helps in estimating the age of a timepiece and also in spotting conversion to later forms of escapement.

The crown wheel is rotated by the weight or spring which drives the clock. All clocks were weight-driven until the invention of the spring motor around 1425. The purpose of the verge is to stop and release the crown wheel at short and definite intervals of time. The pallets are arranged at about a right angle to each other so that they lie in the path of teeth on opposite sides of the crown wheel. Rotation of the crown wheel turns the verge first one way, then the other.

Verges on early clocks were fitted vertically and across the top of the verge arbor was a bar, making it of T shape. This bar is the time

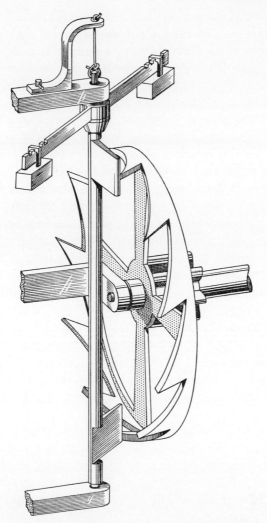

FIG. 7. Verge and foliot escapement with crown wheel.

controller, the essential in any mechanical timekeeper. The bar was rotated backwards and forwards in a small arc by the turning of the crown wheel by the driving weight. A bar oscillated in this way will do so much more freely at one particular frequency, this frequency depending on its moment of inertia. So the rate of oscillation of the bar tended to control the rate of the clock.

The earliest form was a cranked bar with a small weight hung on each end from one of a series of notches. Moving these weights towards the centre decreased the moment of inertia and therefore

93

made the weighted bar oscillate more rapidly, which increased the rate of the clock. Moving them outwards did the opposite. Such an arrangement is called a 'foliot', a word that is probably French in origin, from *folier*, to dance about madly, as it was first used by Jean Froissart (1337–1410) in his famous chronicles. (In fact, the foliot is rather stately in its slow swinging.)

The foliot is a form of balance, the generic name for such time controllers. Another is the wheel balance, or balance wheel, which was in use perhaps as early as, or earlier than, the foliot and is universal today in watches, and non-pendulum clocks.

The foliot, and the verge to which it was attached, were hung from a thread attached to a gallows-shaped bar fastened to the top of the movement. Each end of the verge ran in a hole. The thread could be moved inwards or outwards as an additional and finer means of controlling the rate, the effect being to increase or decrease the friction of the verge against the sides of the holes in which it runs, and therefore the force with which the foliot was oscillated. A verge and foliot is shown in Fig. 7 and also in Plate 1.

A third means of regulation was by adding to or subtracting from the driving weight. Some weights of lantern and chamber clocks had cups in the top, or an open top to the brass casing around the lead weight, to hold lead shot. With careful regulation, it was possible to achieve timekeeping to an order of a quarter of an hour a day.

In spring-driven clocks, which were developed because of their portability, it was obviously impractical to have the same kind of foliot with little weights hanging from the ends. In place, a dumb-bell-shaped foliot was employed. This was not adjustable, so a different form of adjustment was needed to control the rate of the dumb-bell balance.

The adjustment in spring-driven clocks was the 'hog's bristle', which comprised two stiff bristles from a pig, mounted on an arm. As the balance swung to and fro it 'banked' against the springy bristles. The arm on which it was mounted could be moved to alter the arc of swing of the balance and therefore its timekeeping. The balance on these clocks was not suspended from a thread.

The balance wheel, normally a rim with a single spoke, common on early lantern clocks, occasionally had a 'banking pin' to limit the swing of the balance. One can be seen in Plate 10.

Spring-driven clocks in their earliest form had in some cases a variable engagement of the verge pallets with the crown wheel, the movement of the verge staff being caused by a rack arrangement.

WEIGHT DRIVE

A weight falling to the ground, because it is acted upon by the force of gravity, provides an ideal constant driving force, provided that it is not expected to do so while being transported. The very first weights were stones. Stones trimmed to shape and provided with iron loops for attachment to the ropes of the clock can still be seen on some old church clocks, such as that at Northill, in Oxfordshire. From the seventeenth century, for better domestic clocks, cylindrical lead weights in brass casings were usual, and for cheaper productions, cast iron. This continued right through the period of hand-made clocks. Occasionally the weight in pounds was cast into the cast iron. The driving weight for a normal 8-day longcase clock weighs from 12 to 16 pounds, but on very well made clocks, where the friction is low, it may be as light as 8 pounds. The striking train weight is about the same, but sometimes heavier. When in doubt always put the heavy weight on the striking side, i.e. the left from the front. Regulators usually have very light weights.

The going period of clocks is normally related to a natural period of time so that the hours of winding can be habitual. The earliest chamber clocks, however, usually required winding twice a day because of the power needed and the fact that they could not be placed inconveniently high on the wall.

The earliest had two cords wound opposite ways round a drum or barrel. One cord carried the driving weight. As the weight descended, it turned the barrel to drive the clock and also to wind up the other cord. Pulling down this other cord, therefore, raised the weight again. After about 1500, pulleys with V-grooves replaced barrels on domestic clocks. A single cord ran in the groove. The driving weight was attached to one end, and the free end (used to raise the weight, by pulling downwards) had a small weight attached to it to keep it in the pulley groove. Alarm, striking and chiming trains were wound in the same way. Often, the groove was set with stubby spikes to stop the rope from slipping. Pulleys for chains were shaped in the groove to the links, also to prevent slip.

The weight pulley turned a large geared wheel (the great wheel), which turned the clock hand by means of a 'pinion of report'. The great wheel also drove the crown wheel of the verge escapement. When the pendulum came into common use, the wheel train was arranged so that clocks could be made to run for a week or more at one winding.

Because clock owners cannot be depended upon to wind their possessions at the right times, there was always a reserve of running time, and, although this varied, clocks intended to be wound daily

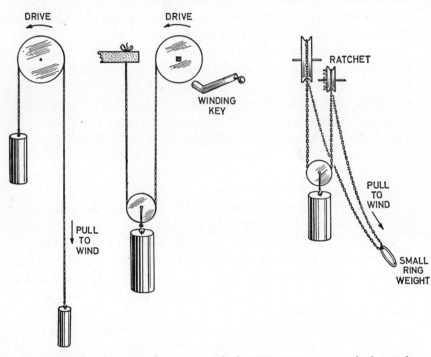

Fig. 8. Weight drives. Left: Lantern clock. Centre: Longcase clock. Right: Huygens' endless chain for 30-hour clocks.

are usually called '30-hour clocks', and those intended to be wound weekly, '8-day clocks'. By suitable gearing, it was possible to make clocks run for longer periods than a week, provided that the friction was low enough to avoid extremely heavy weights that could bend the clock movement and the length of fall for driving was not excessive.

A ratchet arrangement was necessary to wind up the weight. This was part of the pulley attachment to its arbor. Pulling the free end of the cord over the pulley raised the weight, which turned the pulley

1 Salisbury clock of 1386 being restored to verge operation by Smiths of Derby. It can be seen working in Salisbury Cathedral.

2 Early English turret clock at Haddon Hall, Derbyshire. The frame is wooden.

3 Iron chamber, or Gothic clock, of the 16th century with alarm, quarter striking and moon dial.

4 Table clock with original travelling box, by N. Vallin, a Flemish maker working in London from 1598 to 1640.

5 16th century German table clock, earliest known with seconds hand (lower small one). It also has hour and minute hands, calendar and zodiac dials.

6 Automaton clock of *c.* 1615 with
dial and bell in the howdah. The
eyes move at every tick and there are
other movements at the hour.

7 Typical 'Türmchen-Uhr' made in
Augsburg in the first quarter of the
17th century.

6

7

8

8 Crucifix clock made in Augsburg
c. 1610 with stackfreed movement in
the base. A moving ring on the top
shows the hour.

9

9 Lantern, or brass, clock signed
Thos. Tompion, Londini.

10. (a) Lantern clock of *c.* 1650 by
Nicholas Coxeter, London, with
bell and frets removed to show
single spoke balance wheel.

(b) Some lantern clocks (and others)
had alarm dials in the centre.
Hand not original.

11 Hooded clock by Joseph Knibb
between lantern and longcase clock
periods. Engraved tulip pattern dial.

11

10a

10b

12 One of the first
longcase clocks, of
1660–65, by Ahasuerus
Fromanteel, London.
Short, narrow and in
architectural style.

13 Walnut month clock
of *c.* 1680 by Thos.
Tompion. Height
7ft. 1in., 10in. dial.

14 Floral marquetry
clock by Isaac Lowndes,
Pall Mall. It goes for a
month at a winding.

15 Marquetry clock by
Thos. Bridge, London,
of c. 1700. Note convex
moulding under hood
and barley sugar pillars.

16 Clock of c. 1740 by
Isaac Nickals, Wells,
Norfolk, in case of gold
and coloured lacquer.
Tidal dial, moon dial,
day and month dials,
chiming with repeat and
silent controls, and
centre seconds hand.

17 Walnut cased clock
with pagoda top by
Benjamin Gray. Moon
dial, date in arch, month
in seconds ring aperture.

20 'Yorkshire case' in mahogany from end of longcase period. Painted dial shows the Last Supper.

18 Mahogany longcase clock with painted dial and matching hands by Thos. Moor, Salisbury, *c*. 1780. Ting-tang quarters.

19 Mahogany month regulator with all-over silvered dial by John Ellicott, *c*. 1750. Hours in crescent.

21 Early longcase clock dial by
Wm. Clement, London, with
seconds numerals inside divisions,
cherub spandrels, and early hands.

22 Break arch dial from John
Ellicott clock with quarter and half
hour marks omitted, and large
minutes and seconds numerals.

23 One of the first English bracket clocks, in architectural style, with silent
verge escapement, by Wm. Clement, London. Complete with bracket.

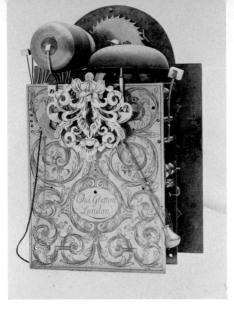

24 Back plate of bracket clock by Charles Gretton, London, with engraved acanthus leaves and elaborately pierced piece over bridge. Note bob pendulum and teeth of calendar disc at the top.

25 Silver-mounted bracket or table clock by Henry Jones, late 17th century. Strikes hours, then repeats them at half-hours on higher toned bell. Pierced chapter ring. Note pillars.

26 Back plate of a bracket clock engraved 'White, Birmingham' but actually made by Thwaites and Reed, London. Hour repeating, anchor escapement and lenticular pendulum. See (30).

27 Bracket clock in tortoiseshell case with basket top by H. Adamson, London, c. 1680.

28 Josiah Emery bracket clock with bell top, on its wall bracket. Rise and fall and strike silent controls on dial.

29 Table clock with early round enamel dial and wavy minute hand in mahogany case, by Edward Tutel, London.

27

28

29

30

30 Front of table clock (26). Painted dial, matching hands, fish-scale frets, repeater cord at side. c. 1820.

31 Musical clock for
the Turkish market
made by George
Clarke. Tune selector
at top. Painted case.
Now in British
Museum.

32 'Director's clock',
a throwback style of
the late 19th century
and early 20th, for
presentation.
This picture is
included for
comparison.

33 Early English dial wall clock with fusee movement, verge escapement, bob pendulum, and longcase style hands.
Diameter about 15 inches.

34 Mahogany balloon clock made *c.* 1810 by Dwerrihouse and Carter, London, with gilt matching hands.

35 Cottage clock with verge watch movement, a cheap production of the 19th century.
Height about 7 inches.

36 Tavern clock, also called 'Act of Parliament clock', of later 18th century. The width of the dial is 2ft. 4in.

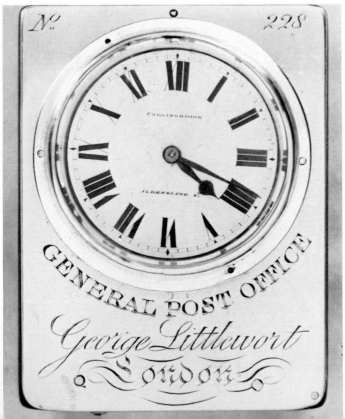

37 Mail guard's watch of 1825–30 issued to the mail guard who sat at the back of a horse-drawn mail coach with blunderbuss and cutlass. Length about 5 inches.

38 Mahogany-cased
regulator with mercury
pendulum but ordinary
dial, popular in the late
19th and early 20th
centuries. This was made
by Samuel Smith,
London.

39 Two-day marine chronometer by Parkinson and Frodsham, London, of about 1830, in its gimbals and mahogany box.

40 Coach clock-watch of the late 18th century by Ferdinand Berthoud. The pendant swivels for hanging.

41 'Sedan chair clock', about 7 in. diameter with 30-hour verge watch movement (like cottage clock, 35). Made c. 1750–60 by Thos. Gorsuch, Shrewsbury.

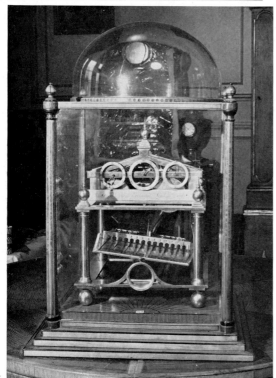

42

44

42 Two ornate French carriage clocks, one a miniature. The small dial on the larger clock is for setting the alarm. This clock is also a repeater.

43 English table clock by Bridgeman and Brindle in carriage clock style, but with chronometer movement and regulator-style dial, showing mean time on upper dial and sidereal on lower.

44 Rolling ball clock invented by Wm. Congreve after 1808, in its glass case. Table on which ball runs is the lower part of the clock. Made by William French, Royal Exchange.

45 Night clock made by Petrus Campanus in 1683. Front pendulum can be seen through dial. Italian made. The time is just after 9.45.

46 French mystery clock of the mid-19th century with glass dial on an ormolu base containing a 'chaffcutter' movement.

47

50

48

47 Lighthouse clock of 1885 which has a torsional pendulum with helical spring showing in the 'cupola'.

48 One of the first 400-day clocks, made by Jahreuhrenfabrik, Germany, in 1885.

49 Industrial Revolution clock of the late 19th century by Sutton, representing a beam engine. The beam is also the balance of the clock movement.

50 Ticket clock made in France about 1920.

51 One of the first electric clocks, invented by Alexander Bain, made for the Electric Telegraph Company about 1840, and operated by 'the new electric fluid'.

52 Bulle electric pendulum clock made in France in the early 20th century.

49

51 52

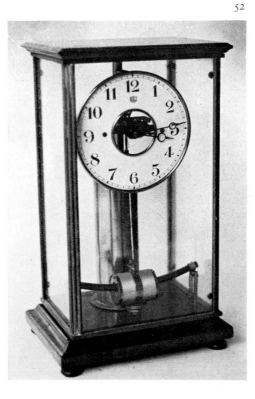

53 Eureka 1000-day electric clock made some time after 1906.

54 Cathedral type of chiming skeleton clock made in the latter part of the 19th century.

55 Small French skeleton clock with alarm in base, sold in great numbers from 1851.

56 Skeleton clock with balance wheel (top left) and going barrel, made in last quarter of 19th century.

57 Water clock often seen in this or similar form. All are novelties. There never was a genuine water clock of this type.

58 Louis XVI ormolu and marble clock, with calendar hand, by Chopin of Paris.

59 French regulator of *c.* 1790 with moon dial at the top and time of day, calendar and zodiac dials below. Barometer in the pendulum.

60 Elaborate embossed and coloured metal pendulum from a French Morbier clock in a country-made viola-shaped case.

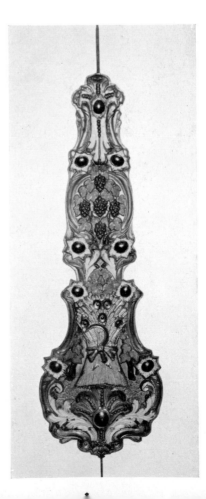

61 Wooden movement
of one of the first cuckoo
clocks, made *c.* 1740 by
Anton Ketterer of the
Black Forest.

62 Wrongly-named
'Dutch' type of shield
of cuckoo clock in (61)
with cuckoo at top.

63 German Telleuhr, or plate clock, with front pendulum, *c.* 1740. In the Science Museum.

64 Cuckoo-quail clock of carved wood cottage style that became typical of the Black Forest.

65 Typical Black Forest clocks in the Mauthe Museum. L. to r.: Wall clock of 1841 with cowstail pendulum; night watchman's clock with push-in pegs, 18th century; metal wall clock, 17th century; and a dial clock with calendar hand, 18th century or later.

65 64

66

66 Austrian Empire temple clock, or Stockuhr, with visible automaton dial showing Vulcan's forge.

67 Vienna regulator by Josef Rommel, Vienna, c. 1840, with month movement and true enamel dial in inlaid mahogany case.

68 Dutch Friesland clock with painted dial on its elaborate wooden wall bracket. In Science Museum.

67

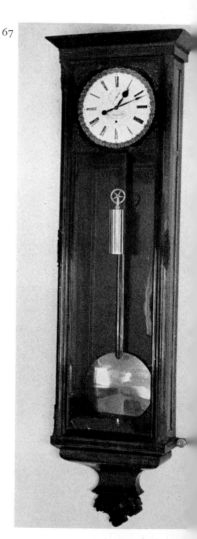

68

69 70

69 Dutch staartklok
which hangs on the wall
and has a seconds
pendulum in the narrow
case behind the exposed
weight.

70 Early (left) and late
styles of verge
escapements in English
bracket clocks. Models
made by Mr Chas.
Hobson of Hove.

71

71 American waggon
spring clock of double
steeple style bearing
name of Birge and
Fuller, Connecticut,
c. 1830–35.

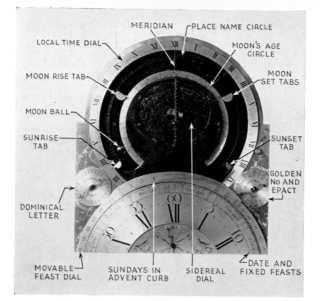

MERIDIAN — PLACE NAME CIRCLE

LOCAL TIME DIAL — MOON'S AGE CIRCLE

MOON RISE TAB — MOON SET TABS

MOON BALL

SUNRISE TAB — SUNSET TAB

GOLDEN No AND EPACT

DOMINICAL LETTER

MOVABLE FEAST DIAL — SUNDAYS IN ADVENT CURB — SIDEREAL DIAL — DATE AND FIXED FEASTS

72 Dial of an exceptionally elaborate astronomical longcase clock in a 9ft. tall case by Thos. Lister, of Halifax, c. 1780.

73 New moon face on a moon dial of a longcase clock by Edward Barlow, Oldham, c. 1750.

74 Longcase clock dial with annual calendar and equation of time indication, by Francis Gregg, Covent Garden, c. 1700.

75 Dial of longcase clock with equation of time work in the arch, made by Thos. Tompion as a gift to the Pump Room, Bath, Som., in 1709. The lever in the slot by III operates maintaining power.

76 Clock-watch with stackfreed movement and 24-hour dial made in Nuremberg *c.* 1550. In Basingstoke Museum.

77 Movement of a 'form watch' in a rock crystal case like an escallop shell, made by Nicolaus Rugendas of Augsberg, *c.* 1610.

78 Early 17th century small watch of Puritan style with oval case and stackfreed movement.

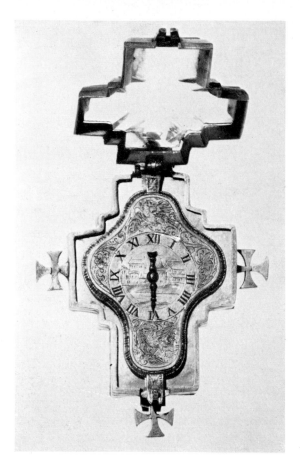

79 A 'form watch' shaped like a cross, with rock crystal front and back. This one is actually a fake. Many such fakes were made.

80 Watch with typical 'feathered' border of English work, *c.* 1610, by Thos. Nixon. In Clockmakers' Company Museum.

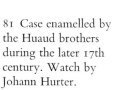

81 Case enamelled by the Huaud brothers during the later 17th century. Watch by Johann Hurter.

82 Movement of watch by Charles Goode, of London, with balance cock covering almost all of back plate.

83 Complete chatelaine with repeating watch by Cabrier, which has a gem-set case, and original key.

84 Repoussé cased watch by Richard Street of 1714. The baroque pattern is appropriate to its date.

85 Complicated watch
by Thos. Mudge of 1757
with grande sonnerie
and minute repeating.
Enamelled dial is typical
of period.

87 Large automaton
watch with musical
cylinder movement, and
half-pearl set bezel.
Automaton includes an
elaborate fountain.

86 Three-cased watch by
Isaac Rogers for the
Turkish market. The
outer case is covered in
shagreen. Note the
watch paper.

88 Self-winding pocket watch made in quantity around 1890. Swinging weight on right.

89 Self-winding watch with rotor that winds in either direction, made in mid-18th century by 'ALR'.

90 Early rack lever escapement watch by Peter Litherland, Liverpool, with going barrel, made in 1792.

92 Small French ring watch which also has a calendar. Made *c.* 1779.

94 One of the first self-winding wrist watches invented by Englishman, John Harwood. It has no winding button.

91 The original 'dollar watch' made in quantity from 1892.

93 Miniature Swiss fully jewelled lever watch on a sixpence, with its winding key.

95 French watch with enamelled cartouche chapters.

96 Swiss automata watch of the 1880s with rocking see-saw on the dial.

97 English equation of time watch by John Ellicott. Extra minute hand shows the difference between mean and solar time. Year calendar round the outside.

98. Back of watch by Le Roy of Paris, 1897, thought to be the most complicated ever made.

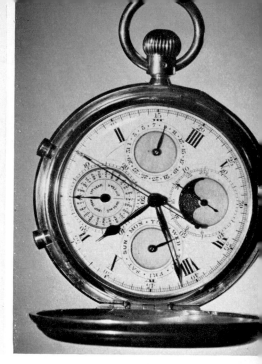

99 100
101 102

99 Complicated watch by Breguet et Fils, of Paris, with up-and-down dial near IIII chapter. Typical Breguet style of dial and hands.

101 Back plate of verge striking watch by William Knottesforde, 1683, showing mainspring set-up dial with worm drive, hairspring regulator, and locking plate with hours on it, on the right.

100 English and Swiss complicated work of about 1920, bearing the name S. Smith and Sons, Strand. (Now Smiths Industries.) Two seconds hands are one above the other; so are the minute-recording and year hands.

102 Watch by Chas. Goode, London, with cock removed to show earlier form of balance spring regulation. Curb pins are moved in arc of balance spring by turning the small dial. See (82).

103

104

105

103 Movement of watch by Barton, of
Newborough, with wedge-shaped balance
cock, diamond end-stone, lever regulator,
and, on the left, the dust cap.

104 Watch of 1819 by J. Moxon with Savage
2-pin lever escapement and regulation index
on the balance cock.

105. Miniature Swiss lever watch with bar
movement.

106 Elaborate coloured watch keys, common in the 18th and 19th
centuries. In Clockmakers' Company Museum.

107 Swiss watch of 1789–1802
period with key and one of the first
production keyless watches. Made
in 1850. On the dial is
'Nicole & Capt., London'.

108 Watch by Joseph Johnson of
Liverpool with typical 'Liverpool
jewelling' (behind the rim of the
balance wheel), made before 1829.

109 Watch of 1906–7 with three-
quarter plate movement and
Bonniksen's karrusel.

110 Watch for telling the time by touch. Made by Le Roy, Paris, in 1810. It shows 8 o'clock.

backwards, but not the clock mechanism, because the pulley 'free-wheeled' in exactly the same way as turning the pedals of a bicycle backwards without driving the bicycle (Fig. 8).

The barrel with two ropes – the contra-barrel – referred to on page 95, as well as the V-pulley, were superseded by reappearance of the barrel, but this time with a single rope or cord wound round it. To the barrel was attached the first gear wheel of the timepiece, called the 'great wheel' or 'main wheel'. In domestic clocks the barrel was turned for winding by means of a cranked key.

In the seventeenth century and after, when clocks became more common, it was usual to use gut for supporting the driving weights, the gut being wound on to barrels with shallow grooves cut in them to prevent the gut lines from crossing when the clock was being wound. Most of these weight-driven clocks were longcase clocks and ran for eight days. Incidentally, red-coloured silk lines were commonly used for regulators.

With such clocks that ran for longer periods came a different drive arrangement, to lessen the fall of the weight and yet provide the same power. One end of the gut line was fastened to a fixed point – actually the seatboard, a horizontal strip of wood supporting the movement in a longcase clock – and the other end to the barrel. The weight hung on a pulley in the loop so formed. By doubling the weight necessary to drive the clock, double the going time was achieved with the same fall. Winding arrangements are shown in Fig. 8.

The eight-day longcase clock is wound by a key through the dial. The key – a cranked key like a winding handle – fits on to a square on the end of a barrel and, when turned clockwise, winds the gut line on to the barrel, to raise the weight.

Very early in the eighteenth century, makers produced occasional month clocks. These had the same fall of weight and some of the finest even the same poundage of weights as eight-day clocks, but another wheel was employed in the timekeeping trains to lower the driving weight more slowly. This meant that the clock was wound by turning the winding key anti-clockwise. This direction of winding is an immediate indication that the clock is out of the ordinary. Three-month clocks were also made very occasionally, and even year clocks. Two-day clocks were very occasionally turned out, by makers seeking novelty, perhaps.

An unusual method occasionally employed to decrease the fall of

G

the weight on long-going time clocks was to mark the dial in two periods of 12 hours so that the hour hand went round once a day instead of twice.

ENDLESS ROPE DRIVE

The weight drives so far described suffered from one disadvantage when applied to accurate clocks. During winding, power was removed from the clock movement which slows or stops. It normally takes between a quarter and half a minute to wind a longcase clock and with an eight-day clock this loss of time during a week is not serious. When a clock is wound daily, however, it can add up to a substantial loss over a period. If the clock were regulated to take it into account, variations in winding time would affect the clock rate.

These variations became apparent when Huygens made a leap forward in accuracy by inventing the pendulum clock in 1657. He was aware of the variations caused by winding and invented at the same time a means of overcoming them, using an endless rope over two ratchet wheels, one of which drove the clock. The weight was hung from a pulley in one of the loops, and the clock was wound by pulling the rope over the second ratchet pulley. The arrangement, shown in Fig. 8, allowed the weight to continue driving while it was being wound. This is known as providing 'maintaining power'.

All normal weight-driven domestic clocks requiring daily winding incorporated Huygens endless rope – or more usually on 30-hour longcase clocks made during the eighteenth and in the nineteenth centuries, endless chain. A current use for this maintaining power is in converting old turret clocks, formerly wound by hand, to automatic winding. An electric motor with a sprocket replaces the winding ratchet pulley. At the bottom of its fall, the weight switches the motor on and at the top switches it off.

SPRING DRIVE

The alternative to weight drive was to use energy stored in a coiled spring, introduced because it enabled the clock to be more portable. A mainspring, however, introduces various complications because the power exerted by a coiled spring alters as it runs down. If wound too tightly, it can become coil-bound, so that its initial power is low or zero. Normally the power output initially is very high and falls off quickly to a level that drops gradually but evenly for the next few hours; then, as the spring is on its last expenditure of power, there is a sudden falling off.

If the oscillating system were perfect, the falling power of the spring would not affect the timekeeping to a serious extent. except at the fully wound and almost run down positions. Unfortunately early mainsprings, made of brass or steel, had very uneven output and the verge and crown wheel with foliot, dumb-bell or wheel balance, was not isochronous.

Isochronism is an important factor in good timekeeping. It means, as it is often expressed, 'keeping equal time in different arcs'. Put another way, a balance, or any other timekeeping system which is isochronous, has the same rate of timekeeping whether it is swinging in an arc of 90 degrees, 250 degrees, or any other arc. An isochronous balance would therefore be independent of the driving force for its timekeeping.

For centuries the search for an isochronous oscillating system has been carried on and only today, in the oscillations of the atom, has it been found, although mechanical timekeepers in the first half of the twentieth century have approached very near to it.

Not having an isochronous oscillating system, it was necessary to make the mainspring provide as even an output as possible. The first attempts to do this incorporated the very sensible scheme of limiting employment of the spring to the middle part of its range, which provided the flattest part of the power output. An arrangement, called 'stopwork', is found in conjunction with other devices on the earliest spring-driven clocks and watches, and is still used today. When the spring was wound up, a toothed wheel on its arbor engaged another toothed wheel in the circumference of which several teeth had not been cut. The gearing between the two toothed wheels was arranged so that the mainspring could not be fully

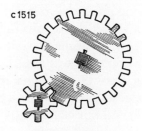

c 1515

FIG. 9. Stopwork.

wound, because the uncut teeth stopped the engaging wheel from turning further. Similarly, the spring was brought to a halt before it was fully run down (Fig. 9).

In conjunction with stopwork, a further device called a 'fusee' or another, called a 'stackfreed', was incorporated. The stackfreed is only found on early German watches. It was a cam rotated by the mainspring as it ran down. A roller on the end of a stiff spring presses on the edge of the cam, the geometry of which was arranged to decrease the friction as the mainspring ran down, thus compensating for the lessening power. Finally, as the mainspring went to the limit

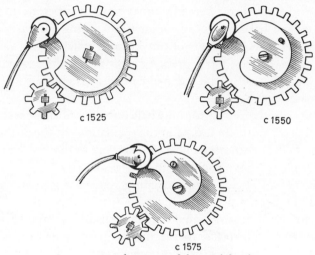

c 1525   c 1550

c 1575

FIG. 10. Development of the stackfreed.

of its lower stop, the friction wheel of the stackfreed ran into a 'parking hollow'. One can be seen in Fig. 10. Early stackfreeds were nearly circular, but as their theory became better understood, their spiral shape became more pronounced until late ones were wedge-shaped. They were made to match the mainsprings with which they were fitted and it became more economical as time went by to save cost on the spring, allowing it to be shorter and thicker and therefore stronger, and to compensate by more powerful action on the stackfreed. The wedge shape was a technological advance of the time because, after the apex of the cam was passed, the stackfreed spring actually assisted the failing power of the mainspring.

Nevertheless, the stackfreed was never a satisfactory device and did not outlast the mid-sixteenth century. Its use was almost confined to southern Germany and to watches. Makers outside, and in other parts of Germany, favoured another device called a 'fusee', a name derived from an old French name for a spindle of thread, which it resembled. The fusee is a very old as well as an efficient device. The principle was known and it was illustrated as early as 1407. It is still in use to this day in marine chronometers and the best spring-driven clocks.

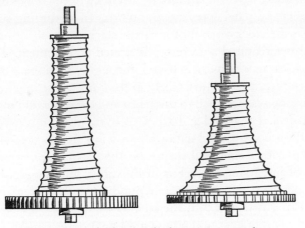

FIG. 11. An early fusee and a later very tapered one.

The purpose of the fusee, a trumpet-shaped drum, is to alter the mechanical advantage of the driving system so that it compensates for the failing power of the mainspring (Fig. 11). Early fusees were not much flared; the curve became more pronounced as clock and watch makers saved costs by fitting cheaper mainsprings with a bigger fall in power output as they ran down.

The first mainsprings were inspired by the weight-driven clock. A flat strip of spring was attached to, and wound around, the arbor carrying the first driving wheel (the main wheel). The outer end of the spring was attached to one of the pillars of the movement. If the arbor were wound in one direction, it would run down in the opposite direction (Fig. 12). A ratchet and pawl arrangement was

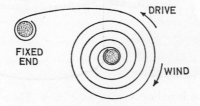

FIG. 12. Earliest form of mainspring.

interposed between the mainwheel and the arbor so that the mainwheel remained stationary as the mainspring was wound.

The system, with its open, unprotected mainspring, is still used today on cheap alarm clocks. It has two main disadvantages. If the open spring breaks, it is likely to wreck the movement, and while the arbor is being wound, the clock or watch stops, because the power is being reversed, although the clickwork (as clockmakers call the ratchet and pawl) prevents the wheels from turning backwards. This was the clockwork motor of the stackfreed.

The fusee required a more sophisticated arrangement. The spring was enclosed in a cylindrical barrel, through which the arbor passed, so that the arbor could turn freely in the barrel. The inner end of the coiled spring was attached to the arbor and the outer end to the inside of the barrel. The barrel and arbor were mounted in the movement so that the arbor was held stationary by a ratchet wheel attached to it, engaging with a click and spring on the plate. The reason for this, instead of just fixing the arbor immovably, will appear shortly.

Around the spring drum was wound a length of gut. Pulling the end of this gut would turn the barrel, winding the spring inside it, so that the spring kept pulling the gut line. It is rather like the weight drive in reverse. The weight tries to unwind the rope from the barrel; the mainspring tries to wind the gut line *on to* the barrel (Fig. 13).

Unfortunately, the pull of the spring is variable, unlike the pull of gravity. Therefore, as the gut is wound off the barrel, it is wound on to the trumpet-shaped fusee, which is grooved for the purpose. Now, as the mainspring drum winds *back* its gut line, the gut line turns the fusee and drives the clock. But when the force of the main-

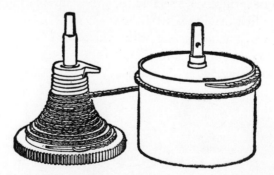

FIG. 13. The fusee and barrel drive with fusee chain. The main spring is coiled inside the barrel.

spring is high, because it is fully wound, it operates on a small radius of the fusee. As its power gradually fails, when running down, so the gut operates on an increasing diameter of the fusee, which increases the leverage and tends to keep the power output constant.

The first toothed driving wheel is on the fusee arbor and attached to the fusee by a click and spring. The fusee can then be turned backwards to wind the gut on to it from the barrel, without rotating the wheels of the train backwards.

The purpose of the ratchet and click on the *barrel* arbor is to 'set up' the mainspring. That is, to make sure that when the clock or watch has run down, the mainspring itself has not run down completely, otherwise the gut would become loose and run off the grooves of the fusee.

Another important function of setting-up the mainspring is for broad regulation of timekeeping. Combined with it is a form of stopwork which limits the extent to which the mainspring can be wound up or is allowed to run down. Altering the point from which the spring can be wound obviously alters the level of its power output and therefore, since no control system is truly isochronous, the amplitude of the balance or pendulum and the rate of going of the clock or watch.

The fusee by itself, like the open mainspring, does not provide maintaining power; i.e. the clock or watch will lose or stop during winding.

The fusee combined with mainspring and barrel was the almost universal motor for clocks from the time the mainspring was invented until the nineteenth century. For watches, it was also almost universal until about the same time. The early gut was replaced after about 1630 by chain for spring-driven table clocks. The chain was

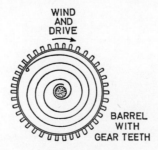

WIND
AND
DRIVE

BARREL
WITH
GEAR TEETH

FIG. 14. The going barrel. When the central arbor is wound, the drive through the teeth is in the same direction.

made up of links like a bicycle chain, the earliest fusee chains having long links. Techniques of making fusee chains improved until they were small enough to be used in watches by the last quarter of the sixteenth century.

The fusee was finally ousted by the 'going barrel' which became practicable because of improvements over the centuries in mainsprings, escapements, and oscillating systems.

The going barrel works in this manner (Fig. 14). The coiled mainspring that drives the clock (or watch) has its inner end fixed to an arbor. Over the spring is placed a cup, called the 'barrel', which can turn freely on the arbor. The outer end of the spring is attached to the inside of the barrel. If now the barrel is held, and the arbor rotated, this will wind up the mainspring. If the barrel is released it will rotate in the same direction as the arbor was wound. Therefore, the barrel will always continue to go in the same direction as the arbor is wound.

When wound (by a key), the arbor is prevented from turning backwards by a ratchet arrangement. The barrel itself acts as a wheel, having teeth cut around its edge to drive the gears of the clock. A similar system is employed in going barrel watches. The going barrel provides its own maintaining power.

11 Keeping Time

WE TURN now to the control system and escapement part of the
clock. In the pendulum clock invented by Huygens, and made by
clockmaker Salomon Coster, a verge and crown wheel escapement
was employed with a pendulum controller, as shown in Fig. 15. The
actual clock is small, for hanging on the wall, with a short pendulum,
and is kept in Leyden, Holland. A copy of it can be seen in the
Science Museum, London. The pendulum is suspended from a
double thread on each side of which are two curved plates called
'cycloidal cheeks'.

Huygens was a mathematician and astronomer, an intellectual
giant of his time, and he had found that not even the pendulum is
truly isochronous. It had been discovered earlier by Galileo that a
pendulum apparently takes the same time to swing from side to side
whether it swings in a big arc or a small one, and whether the bob
weight on the end is heavy or light. The only thing that affects its
time of swing is the effective length.

Galileo was right, said Huygens, provided that the pendulum is
swinging not in an arc but in a cycloidal curve. A cycloidal path is
that traced by a point on the rim of a rolling wheel. He provided his
cycloidal cheeks to constrain the pendulum in this path, but in
practice they were useless. They were, however, used later by clockmaker John Harrison for another purpose, to reduce timekeeping
errors caused by variations in temperature.

VERGE AND PENDULUM

Makers of spring-driven clocks in England adopted the pendulum
almost immediately after it was invented, but abandoned Huygen's
refined principles and attached the pendulum rod directly to the

verge arbor. The front end of the verge arbor, behind the dial, runs in a pivot hole, and the other end, beyond the pendulum rod ends in a V slot which rocks in a wider V slot. The verge escapement with pear-shaped bob pendulum was used in some bracket clocks until as late as about 1800, despite developments which considerably improved the accuracy of longcase clocks. Early verges in bracket

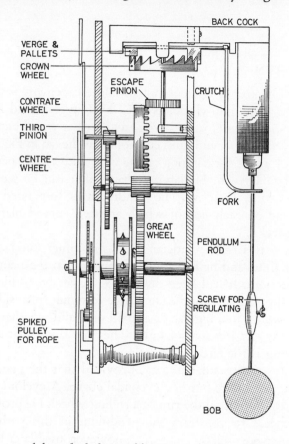

FIG. 15. First pendulum clock designed by Huygens and made by Coster in 1657

clocks were mounted slightly differently, which is an identification feature of early date. (See Plate 70.) Some night clocks were made with 'silent escapements', gut 'bows' replacing the steel pallets.

The first longcase clocks, after they came into fashion in England around 1665, had movements like bracket or table clocks with short pendulums. It was discovered that a long pendulum would have more domination over the clock than a short one. The verge, however, needed a big arc of swing and, if the pendulum were made longer, its arc demanded an exceptionally wide case. It was possible to reduce the arc of swing, and the French did so in some of their clocks, but in England an invention of about 1670 solved both problems in a simple manner and began the ascendancy of the English industry throughout most of the eighteenth century. This was the anchor escapement, attributed to clockmaker William Clement, and scientist Robert Hooke, but which could have been developed as a result of experiments with the cross-beat verge escapement by Knibb.

ANCHOR ESCAPEMENT

The anchor escapement had a flat escape wheel with teeth cut in the edge, but the teeth were similar in shape to those of the crown wheel,

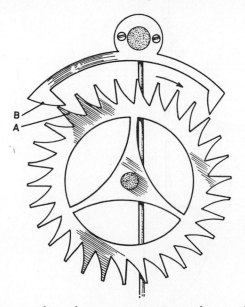

FIG. 16. The anchor escapement. A – tooth. B – pallet.

as shown in Fig. 16. Instead of two pallets along a verge, two pallets were arranged in the same plane. The principle was exactly the same, but the escapement became two dimensional, as it were, instead of 3-D.

The effect of this was for the pallets to span a much smaller number of teeth and for the arc through which the escapement worked to be much less. A pendulum and verge usually works through an arc of 50 degrees and a pendulum and anchor through 5 degrees or so. (The French variation of the verge for pendulum operation had brought down the arc to about 12 degrees.)

The anchor is so-named because of the shape of the arms holding the pallets. It was fixed to an arbor which ran in pivot holes at each

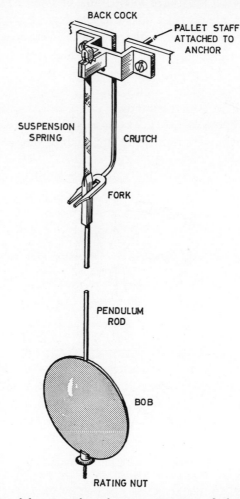

FIG. 17. Pendulum, crutch, and spring suspension of a longcase clock.

end, not in a V slot like the verge. Also, Huygens' original suspension for the pendulum was revived. The pendulum was hung from a fixed point and was connected to the anchor escapement by a crutch. The arrangement is shown in Fig. 17.

Instead of a thread for suspending the pendulum, a short length of spring steel was employed to keep the pendulum length invariable, as it had no stretch like the thread. Thread suspension, usually called 'silk suspension', continued to be used on the continent, particularly by French makers for mantel clocks with pendulums.

With spring suspension, the normal means of altering the rate is to raise or lower the pendulum bob, which rests on a nut, called the 'rating nut'. Throughout the life of longcase clocks, the pendulum rod was a length of iron wire. At the top end was a small brass block into which the suspension spring was fitted, and at the other another, a longer brass block on which the bob weight could slide. At the end of this lower block was another length of rod which had been threaded and on to which the rating nut, often a square one, was screwed. The bob itself was made of lead covered back and front (front only on cheaper clocks) with brass for better appearance and lenticular-shaped, i.e. like a discus.

The upper brass block was the part on which the crutch worked. The top of the suspension spring carried another small piece of brass shaped to hang on a bracket from the back of the clock. (See Fig. 17.) How to remove and replace a pendulum is described in the last chapter.

Towards the end of the eighteenth century, the anchor and spring suspension system came into general employment on bracket and table clocks (Plate 26) which had so long persisted with the atavistic bob pendulum.

The anchor escapement made the seconds pendulum possible. It was found at this time that a long pendulum seemed to provide better timekeeping than a short one and various experiments were made, not only with seconds pendulums of about a metre long, but pendulums about 61 inches long, about the maximum that could be accommodated in a longcase clock, swinging from one side to the other in $1\frac{1}{4}$ seconds. The seconds pendulum was so practical that it became standard, although the longer one was less susceptible to timekeeping variations when the temperature changed.

RECOIL ACTION

Looking at Fig. 16, it will be seen that as the anchor escapement is rocked first to one side and then the other, it will release a tooth of the escape wheel at one side and then the other, at the swing of the pendulum. Each tooth is therefore held up twice as the clock weight, through the train of gears, tries to turn the escape wheel. Escape wheels were normally cut with 30 teeth so that as the pendulum beats seconds, i.e. swings from side to side in a second and releases a tooth at the end of each swing, the escape wheel makes one complete rotation in 60 seconds. This was a very convenient arrangement because a seconds hand could be attached directly on to the end of the escape wheel arbor. It was an almost invariable practice of longcase clock makers.

There are two components in the action of an escapement which can perhaps best be understood by looking at the anchor a little more closely. The function of the controller, in this case the pendulum, is to impose its own rate on the clock. It has, however, to be kept in motion by the clock. It has to be part of it, yet independent of it. In the case of the anchor, the pallets and teeth are so shaped that, as a tooth is released and moves under a pallet, it gives the pallet a small push in passing. This is called the 'impulse' and its purpose is to keep the pendulum swinging. If there were no impulse, the pendulum, and therefore the clock, would come to a stop. If there were too strong an impulse, the pendulum would swing in too great an arc and the pallets would damage themselves on the escape wheel. In each case, timekeeping would suffer.

The geometry of the pallets and teeth is therefore so arranged that if the pendulum swings too widely, it is braked. In other words after an impulse is given, there is a braking effect on the pendulum, known as the 'recoil'. Recoil can be seen by watching the seconds hand of a longcase clock. After it jumps, as a tooth of the escape wheel is released, it moves slightly backwards, or recoils before it jumps forward again at the next second. This does not mean, of course, that the pendulum itself is brought to a sudden recoiling halt at the end of each swing, only the movement.

Briefly the action is this. As the pendulum swings, say, to the left, the entry pallet on the left (see Fig. 16) lifts up to release a tooth of the escape wheel. The anchor spans seven and a half teeth, so that, at this moment, the exit pallet on the right is between two teeth and moving downwards into the path of the tooth on its immediate left. The escape wheel, now freed, makes a sudden jump clockwise until this tooth hits the exit pallet, making the 'tick' sound. But this does not bring the pendulum to an immediate halt. It continues swinging to the left. It is from this point that recoil occurs, because the shape of the pallets and teeth is such that this further movement of the pendulum turns the escape wheel slightly backwards, which is why the escapement is sometimes called the 'recoil escapement'. The pendulum then comes to a halt and swings in the opposite direction, repeating the action with the opposite pallets.

CIRCULAR ERROR

The perfect pendulum should swing in a cycloidal path, as Huygens discovered, but this was difficult to realize in practice. A pendulum swinging in a normal arc is subject to what is called 'circular error'. If the arc of swing increases, the clock begins to lose time. If the arc falls off, the clock begins to gain. Circular error can be avoided by keeping the arc of the pendulum constant.

The anchor and pendulum represented an enormous step forward in accurate timekeeping. The old iron chamber clock with a foliot could be kept to about 10 minutes a day; a bracket clock with verge and bob pendulum to ± 20 seconds a day over short periods; and the long pendulum clock with anchor escapement to ± 10 seconds a day, and even to that number of seconds a week if well made and carefully regulated.

DEAD–BEAT ESCAPEMENT

Even this was not enough for the astronomers of the time, although more than enough for domestic purposes. Demands for even more accuracy led George Graham, a clockmaker who also specialized in scientific instruments, to invent the anchor escapement without

FIG. 18. A dead-beat escapement. Half only of escape wheel shown.

recoil, usually called the 'dead-beat escapement', because the seconds hand remained dead (without recoil) between beats (i.e. ticks). The dead-beat escapement required much more accuracy in manufacture and, after it was invented in 1715, was used for special longcase clocks and for regulators (Fig. 18).

In some versions the pallets are adjustable; in some late regulators they are made of agate or ruby. Graham's dead-beat remained the ultimate in escapements for domestic clocks until recent times when it was overtaken by the lever escapement described on page 165, but it is still used in some master pendulum clocks today.

MAINTAINING POWER

A clock for accurate timekeeping, such as one with a dead-beat escapement, had to have maintaining power to avoid losses during winding. The clock would be wound weekly or monthly and one of two forms of maintaining power was employed. For domestic clocks the more usual was bolt and shutter, invented towards the end of the seventeenth century before the dead-beat escapement. The keyhole or keyholes in the dial were covered by small shutters behind the dial (see Plate 21). Before the winding key could be inserted, the shutter had to be moved aside by pressing down a lever at the side of the movement in early longcase clocks with lift-up hood. After the rising hood went out of use just before 1700, and the hood which slid forward became universal, and the bolt and shutter mechanism was operated by pulling a cord that hung down behind the door in the trunk of the longcase. Moving this shutter aside caused a spring-loaded lever to press against a tooth of one of the wheels in the going train, which kept the clock going for two or three minutes, by which time winding would have been complete.

Another form of maintaining power was devised by John Harrison, pioneer of marine timekeepers. It was invented for spring-driven clocks, being combined with the fusee, although it was also suitable for weight drives and used on regulators. The principle was the same, to apply power by means of a small spring during winding. The mainspring or weight does not drive the clock train direct, but does so through a secondary spring which it compresses. When the main power supply is suspended during winding, the small amount of energy stored in this secondary spring is sufficient to drive the clock for a short time.

Huygens' endless rope drive and also the going barrel provide their own maintaining power.

TEMPERATURE COMPENSATION

Both Harrison and Graham discovered that their accurate clocks were affected by temperature changes and Harrison, although he

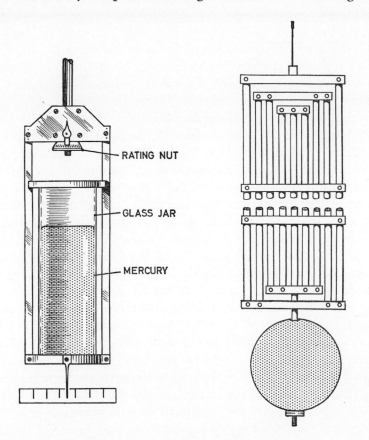

RATING NUT

GLASS JAR

MERCURY

FIG. 19. Pendulum temperature compensation. Left: Graham's mercury bob. Right: Harrison's grid-iron pendulum rod.

started life as a carpenter, carried out elaborate experiments, worthy of any scientist, by which he measured the coefficients of expansion of brass and steel. Then he devised a pendulum made of brass and steel rods so fitted and joined that the expansion of the steel in one direction compensated for the expansion of the brass in the other.

H

The pendulum rod therefore remained the same length regardless of the temperature of the day (Fig. 19).

Harrison's pendulum was known as the 'gridiron' because of its row of bars. It was taken up particularly by the French who used it not only legitimately, but as a decorative feature of small clocks.

Graham also experimented and employed the same principle, but his pendulum carried a jar of mercury which expanded upwards to compensate for the pendulum rod's expansion downards. (See Plate 38 and Fig. 19.) This, too, was taken up by makers on the continent, often with two mercury jars to form the pendulum bob. Some of these were false and entirely decorative. Another arrangement, invented by John Ellicott, had an ingenious arrangement of levers by which differential expansion raised the bob.

On regulator clocks made later in the eighteenth, through the nineteenth and into the twentieth centuries, zinc tube compensation was used. The principle was the same, but a steel rod or tube was used for downwards expansion and a zinc tube to compensate for upwards expansion. Cheaper regulators had pendulum rods made of wood. A straight-grained length of pine, fir, mahogany, or other wood was chosen. It was weathered, dried out, and was then soaked in paraffin wax or varnished to seal it against moisture. Even a wooden rod will lengthen slightly in hot weather, so the leaden bob was fastened to the rod at a point near the bottom of the bob. The top of the bob would expand upwards more than the lower part would expand downwards, thus compensating for the rod. The bob in this case was cylindrical, not lenticular. English regulators almost always have cylindrical bobs to avoid the variations that can be caused by a lenticular bob that twists while swinging. Continental regulators frequently have lenticular bobs. (See Plates 59 and 67.)

Although bracket clocks continued with the verge and pendulum long after the anchor and pendulum was introduced for longcase clocks, occasionally a version of the anchor escapement known as the tic-tac escapement was employed with a bob pendulum by some makers on early bracket clocks. This has a tiny anchor extending over only one and a half or two and a half teeth. The French used it more extensively than the English.

GRAVITY ESCAPEMENT

From about 1760, a few makers tried to develop gravity escapement. without great success. They included Cumming, Mudge, and Reids The object of the gravity escapement was to apply the impulse to the pendulum by a weighted lever instead of by a tooth of the escape wheel. The lever was raised by an escape wheel tooth and released by the swinging pendulum. The belief, a correct one, was that the lever, acting under gravity, would give a more regular impulse than the teeth of an escape wheel subject to variations in the workmanship of the train of gears.

The first successful gravity escapement was not made until about 1852, by E.B. Denison, MA, QC, a lawyer and amateur clockmaker of dominating personality who later became Lord Grimthorpe. On the proposal to build a tower clock for the new parliamentary buildings at Westminster, E. B. Denison, with the practical help of clockmakers E. J. Dent and his son Frederick, manœuvred into the controlling position and bulldozed his gravity escapement and other ideas through all opposition. The result was the highly successful clock, now called 'Big Ben' after the nickname for its hour bell, which was set going in 1859.

The need for such an escapement was greatest on large public clocks because wind blowing on the hands could affect the time-keeping with most escapements. With a gravity escapement, however, it is possible to provide as much extra power as necessary to drive the hands without affecting the timekeeping which is controlled by the constant force applied by the gravity arms.

A device that applies a separate controlled force to impulse a pendulum or balance is called a 'remontoire'. The gravity escapement is one version of it. French clockmakers in the eighteenth and early nineteenth centuries invented various types of remontoire for portable clocks, using the force of a small additional spring which was re-cocked to provide impulse, instead of a gravity lever. A clock with this kind of movement can be valuable.

PIN-WHEEL ESCAPEMENT

For many of the better longcase clocks, and regulators, the French used a pin-wheel escapement, instead of the anchor, which also gave a small arc of swing. The principle is similar but the pallets work at a

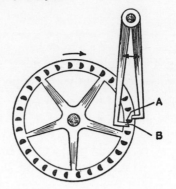

Fig. 20. The pin-wheel escapement. A – pin. B – lever.

tangent to an escape wheel with pins instead of teeth, as shown in Fig. 20, so it is easily recognizable. It was invented by Amant in 1741, and was also employed at times with short pendulums, as in some skeleton clocks.

A variation of the pin–wheel found very occasionally is called the 'coup perdu', or missing tick. One of the pallet arms is hinged in such a way that the pendulum swings without releasing the escape wheel. By this means, seconds can be registered at each movement of a hand with a half-seconds pendulum.

BROCOT ESCAPEMENT

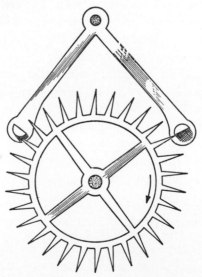

Fig. 21. Brocot's pin-pallet escapement.

For the many marble mantel clocks they made in the early nineteenth century, the French favoured a visible escapement – a visible escape wheel and form of anchor escapement in front of the dial under the 12 chapter. This was a 'pin-pallet', with semi-circular pallets, combined with a short pendulum. It was a modification by Paul Brocot in 1849 of an invention of Achille Brocot some fifty years earlier, the first having a pointed tooth escape wheel and the later one an escape wheel with curved backs to the teeth (Fig. 21). It is usually known as a 'Brocot escapement'. These marble clocks were very popular in Victorian times, and kept good time, partly because they were too heavy to be moved when the mantelpiece was dusted!

GRASSHOPPER ESCAPEMENT

An escapement that was efficient and effective but had a short life was the grasshopper, invented by John Harrison and incorporated first in longcase clocks and later in his marine timekeepers. It was made largely of wood and was difficult to adjust. Later, in the early nineteenth century, it was modified and used by B. L. Vulliamy, the Royal clockmaker of the time.

12 Sounding Time

ALARMS

ALARMS are as old as timekeepers themselves. The first were extremely simple. A rotating dial had a peg inserted in it at the approximate hour or half-hour and this peg tripped a lever which released a weight. The weight descended and operated a verge and pallet arbor carrying a hammer which, swinging to and fro, rang a bell. It may be that this arrangement predated the verge and foliot, which was developed from it. The same principle was incorporated in early chamber clocks and in lantern clocks, but instead of using pegs, which could be lost, a small subsidiary dial was fitted in the centre of the main one. This dial was marked with hours and half-hours, or finer divisions, and was friction tight to the hour hand so that the two rotated together. It was used on both one-hand and two-hand clocks, but the hour hand always had a tail (Plate 10b).

The alarm was set by rotating the alarm disc so that the tail of the hour hand pointed to the time the alarm was required. It had to be rotated clockwise, usually by inserting a peg in one of the holes provided, to act as a handle, but sometimes by projections round the edge. Its operation was the same as the pin which was carried round in the earlier alarm. The disc carried another disc behind the dial with a notch in its edge which released the alarm train as it passed a lever.

A few early alarms were more dramatic and fired a charge of gunpowder in the manner of a flintlock pistol. Such devices were used for time delay fuses in warfare. Another early alarm was a separate device which could be attached to the dial of an early table clock with a horizontal dial, and was operated by the hour hand.

STRIKING HOURS

The earliest form of striking was to sound a single note on a bell at

118

every hour. A pin on an hour wheel rotated so that the pin tripped a lever hourly. The lever moved a spring-loaded hammer, which struck a bell. The earliest mechanism which enabled a clock to sound an actual hour, rather than a time interval, was the locking plate (or to give it its less usual, but more accurate name, the 'count wheel'). One of these can be seen in Fig. 22.

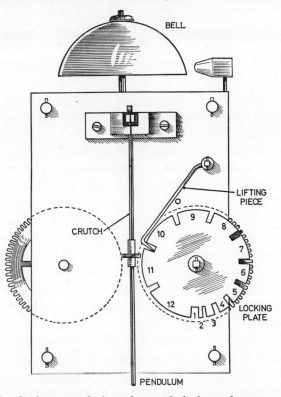

FIG. 22. Back of a longcase clock with outside locking plate. Later ones were between the plates.

The count wheel has round its edge a number of notches. The distance between the notches determines the number of blows to be struck by the bell hammer.

On the earliest clocks, a pin on the great wheel turned once an hour, releasing the striking, but this made setting the clock to time an annoying procedure. If fast, the clock had to be stopped until it indicated the correct time. If slow, it had to be tripped so that it ran down quickly until the correct time was shown by the hands. A special tripping lever was provided. The problem was solved towards

119

the middle of the sixteenth century by providing a slipping clutch to set the hands without interfering with the going of the clock, and by fitting a 12-pointed star wheel to the arbor of the hour hand, which rotated once in 12 hours.

At every hour a point of the star lifts a lever which releases the striking train of gears, driven by a separate weight or spring. The main driving wheel on the striking barrel carries a series of pins to operate the hammer. At the other end of the gear train is a rotating fan, called a 'fly', which acts as a governor to measure out the interval between the blows on the bell. The count wheel is rotated during striking.

A lever, called the 'locking lever', over the edge of the count wheel, is lifted and dropped by the mechanism at each blow of the bell until it drops into one of the slots, when striking stops. Thus it may be seen that the greater the distance apart of the slots, the greater the number of blows struck. A 12-hour count wheel has eleven slots. At one o'clock the locking lever is raised and, after one blow on the bell, drops straight back into the same slot. At two o'clock the locking lever is raised, but, after the first blow, it drops on the edge of the count wheel, so that another blow is struck; then after the second stroke it drops into a slot, so on, round to twelve (Fig. 22).

The star wheel release continued to be used on cheap country clocks with one hand made throughout the eighteenth century.

When the minute hand was introduced, it was given the job of releasing the striking train because of its greater timekeeping accuracy, so a single pin was fastened to the minute wheel (the gear wheel attached to the minute hand), which released the striking train.

The count wheel does not actually *lock* the striking train (despite its usual name of 'locking plate'). This is done in some clocks with locking plates by another wheel, called a 'hoop wheel', which has an incomplete hoop or band attached to its side to form a slot into which drops a hook-shaped lever attached to the locking lever. There is a further arrangement called 'the warning' operated by a pin on the hoop wheel. It releases the striking train a short time before the hour is due to be struck, but holds it up until the actual hour. It can be heard in operation on almost any striking clock.

Locking plate striking has the disadvantages that the number of hours struck can become out of phase with the time shown. Striking can be put into phase by lifting the locking lever by hand to let the striking train run until it agrees with the hands.

By having a 24-pointed star on the hour wheel, or two pins instead of one on the minute wheel, some clocks were made to strike a single note at the half-hours as well as hours. The notches in the count wheel were widened so that the locking lever dropped back into the same slot at each half-hour. French clocks often have such a system.

RACK STRIKING

Locking plate or count wheel mechanisms were used on large numbers of French, American, and Black Forest clocks through the eighteenth century, but as early as 1676 a rival system appeared, invented by the Reverend E. Barlow, an ingenious clockmaker. It was rack-striking, which could not become out of phase with the

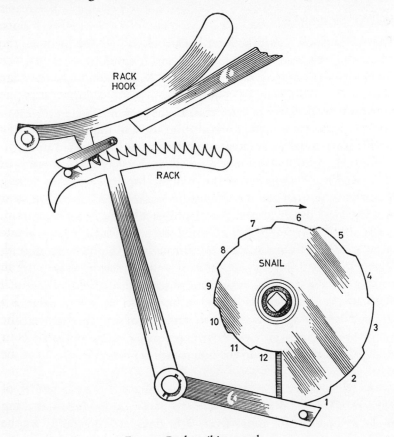

FIG. 23. Rack striking work.

hour and had another considerable value at a time when artificial lighting was ineffective – it could be made to repeat the hour at will. Rack-striking came into gradual use for better clocks by English makers, while the locking plate continued to be incorporated in more standard and in many provincial productions.

The rack system comprises a snail-shaped cam rotating with the hour hand, which determines the number of blows struck, and the rack itself, an ⌐-shaped lever with teeth cut along the top. Just before the hour, the tail of the lever drops on to the edge of the cam, and as the blows are struck on the bell, a rotating pallet winds the rack back to its original position by 'gathering' the teeth one by one. The position of the snail determines how far the rack drops and therefore how many blows are struck (Fig. 23).

REPEATING CLOCKS

To make a clock repeat the hour last struck, it was only necessary to release the rack, and the striking mechanism would operate. Repeating clocks were first operated by a lever. Making the repeater work caused the striking train to run down, of course, although a longer run was provided to allow for this. In the eighteenth century many bracket clocks were made for bedroom use and these had repeating mechanisms, usually operated by pulling a cord from the side of the clock, but no normal striking to awaken the sleeper. In some cases there was no mainspring to be wound for the repeater. It was powered by a small spring wound up as the cord was pulled. The best repeaters usually had a cord from each side of the clock.

The simplest repeaters just repeated the hours, such bracket clocks being made for more general use through the eighteenth century. Most seventeenth-century repeaters gave the quarters as well, however. In the eighteenth century, more sophisticated clocks repeated the half-quarters, the five minutes, and even in a few cases, the minutes. Repeating work was also applied considerably to watches. Many French carriage clocks with repeating work operated by a small button were made in the nineteenth century.

ROMAN STRIKING

In clocks that ran for more than eight days, striking trains were a problem because of the large number of blows that had to be struck during one period of winding, about five thousand in a month clock. To reduce the fall of the weight, Joseph Knibb invented Roman striking, of which Roman numerals were the basis. A blow on a deep bell meant V and a blow on a higher bell I. Thus one blow on the deep bell followed by two on the higher one was VII or seven o'clock – three strokes did the duty of seven. Two strokes on the deeper bell indicated X. This was a sophisticated form of the earlier ting-tang chime described below. Roman striking clocks are rare.

HALF-HOUR STRIKE

The simplest form of indicating fractions of an hour was that adopted by French clockmakers and continued through to the nineteenth century when many cheap versions of earlier French clocks were being manufactured. It consisted simply of sounding a single note on the hour bell at each half-hour – 'half-hour strike' is the correct name. Occasionally a bell of a different tone was used or blows on two bells together.

CHIMES

To chime is to sound the fractions of an hour on more than one bell. The earliest form of striking was the ting-tang on two bells, one of a higher note than the other. It came into use very early in clock history and was employed on at least one of the remaining seventeenth-century longcase clocks. At a quarter past an hour, a single ting-tang was sounded, i.e. a higher note followed by a lower one. At the half-hour there were two ting-tangs; at the three-quarters, three; and at the hour, four ting-tangs followed by the number of hours on a third bell with a deeper note, the hour bell.

Chimes are generally classified by the number of bells on which they are struck. Thus the ting-tang is a two-bell chime. Chimes were made with three, four, five, six, seven, eight, and more bells, thirteen being not uncommon, although perhaps seven and eight were most favoured. Often these just ran through musical scales, once for the first quarter, twice for the second, and so on.

Westminster chimes are much later than popularly believed. The chime, on four bells, was first arranged for St Mary's Church, Cambridge, by Mr Crotch and Dr Jowett in 1793-4, and known as the 'Cambridge chime'. It became popular after its incorporation in the Westminster Palace clock, 'Big Ben', in 1859. The melody is taken from the fifth bar of Handel's *Messiah*, 'I know that my Redeemer liveth.'

The Whittington chime in full is on eight bells and is similar to the sound of Bow Bells, which are supposed to have called back Dick Whittington to become Lord Mayor of London.

GRANDE SONNERIE

A chime like the ting-tang is called 'English striking' or 'petite sonnerie' in France. Grande sonnerie is sounding the hour after each quarter has been struck. Grande sonnerie was never common, but it occurs on both bracket and, more rarely, longcase clocks of English make in the eighteenth century, and particularly in Austria at the end of the eighteenth and beginning of the nineteenth centuries, where it was called the 'Vienna strike'. It was even incorporated in some French carriage clocks, however.

CHIME OPERATION

Both spring and weight-driven clocks were made with chiming trains. A separate weight or spring and a separate train of gears was needed for chiming. It was normally placed on the right with the striking train on the left and timekeeping train in the middle. A chiming clock can be recognized at a glance by the three winding holes.

A chiming train is normally let off by the time train, and the chiming train releases the hour striking train at the hour. In English bracket and longcase clocks, quarter striking is performed by a quarter rack which releases a pin barrel to operate the hammers which strike the bells. In Westminster chimes, for example, there are four gongs and a barrel with twenty pins to operate the four quarters, each of which repeats the previous phrase of music and adds another. The hours are struck on a separate bell of deeper note.

Some late longcase clocks of the nineteenth century have tubular chimes, arranged in a row across the back of the clock. American and German clocks often have rods as gongs, the American ones being coiled.

DUTCH STRIKING

Chiming suffers from the disadvantage that it does not indicate which hour has passed and this was responsible for what is known as Dutch striking. Two bells were employed, one of higher pitch than the other. The hour was struck on the low bell, first quarter on the high one, the half-hour by sounding the number of strokes of the *next* hour on the high bell, and the third quarter by a single note on the low bell.

DOUBLE STRIKING

French provincial clocks from all over the country have the peculiarity of striking the hour twice with an interval of two minutes between them. This applied also to public clocks, and to clocks from northern Italy, where the practice may have originated.

MUSICAL CLOCKS

Chiming clocks playing a tune might well be called musical clocks, but the term should perhaps be reserved for clocks that have a separate musical train of gears for playing a tune, in addition to chiming and striking. The earliest domestic musical clock known is at present on loan to the Victoria and Albert Museum, London. It is spring-driven, probably Flemish, and is dated about 1560.

Not all clocks play on bells. Organ clocks were made at an early period and there is an interesting record of one made and set up for the Sultan of Turkey in 1599 by a Lancashire clockmaker called Randolf Bull as a present from Queen Elizabeth. A variation of the organ clock was the flute-playing clock. Even harp-playing clocks were made in the eighteenth century. The bell, however, was by far the most popular 'instrument' although rods, and, at the end of the nineteenth century, tubes, were sometimes employed instead. For musical watches, reeds like those in a music box were first used for tune-playing.

Bach, Handel, Haydn, Mozart (e.g. 'Orgelstück für eine Uhr'), Beethoven, Rossini, and Schubert, are all known to have written special pieces for carillons of bells and for flute and organ clocks.

13 Moon, Tidal, and other Dials

SUBSIDIARY dials with hands are sometimes seen on clocks, particularly in the corners of those with square dial plates or in the top of break-arch dials. Usually they relate to some auxiliary mechanism of the clock, the most common being Strike–Silent, a dial so marked with a hand that can be turned to silence the striking when necessary (Plate 74).

A similar dial is associated with musical clocks. The hand can be turned to the engraved name of the tune, or to a number, to select that next to be played. Tune selectors were frequently placed in a dial arch (Plate 31).

A subsidiary dial that appeared on the dial of a number of pendulum clocks was for regulation. It raised or lowered the pendulum without having to alter the rating nut below the bob. On English clocks it was usually in a top corner and engraved like a seconds dial from 0 to 60. Turning the hand clockwise increased the rate of the clock by raising the pendulum appropriately to the dial indication. Such devices are also called 'rise and fall' regulators (Frontispiece). The pendulum spring passed through a narrow slot formed by 'chops' and the amount suspended below the chops was the effective length.

French clocks have pendulum regulation, but by a simpler system. The pendulum was hung by a hook on a loop of silk. One end of the silk thread was fixed and the other wound round an arbor, so that turning the arbor raised or lowered the pendulum. On some clocks this was done by a key from the front of the clock at the top of the dial (the square which is turned can just be seen in Plate 58), and on others by a thumb nut at the back of the movement.

The French also had a system, invented by Brocot, similar to that described in the previous paragraph except that a block slid up or down the suspension spring of the pendulum to alter the effective length.

Alarm dials, another ancillary indication, were referred to in Chapter 12. These were normally concentric with the hands, and turned with the hour hand (Plate 10a), but were occasionally separate as on French carriage clocks, a hand being provided to set the time of alarm (Plate 42). This involved a complication in the mechanism as the dial had to remain stationary instead of turning with the hour hand.

Rare on clocks, but standard on marine chronometers, was an up-and-down dial (Plate 39). This showed the extent to which the mainspring had run down, a very important consideration in a marine chronometer which, when used for navigation could mean shipwreck if it stopped. Such dials were marked from 0 up to the number of hours the chronometer would run – 0 to 48 for example in a two-day chronometer – and indicated 0 when the spring was fully wound. The mechanism is simple with a fusee clock or chronometer, which is wound up one way and runs down the other. Up-and-down dials for going barrel timekeepers, such as on some watches of more recent years, require epicyclic gearing.

CALENDARS

One of the simplest additions to a clock was a calendar indicating the day of the month, a very useful service in days when there were no daily newspapers, regularly delivered, and no radio. (The first daily, the *Universal Register*, a forerunner of *The Times*, appeared in 1785.)

In English clocks it was most usual to show the date through a small aperture in the dial (Plates 21 and 22). The mechanism was very simple. Numbers from 1 to 31 were engraved (or painted on many clocks after about 1800) on the front of a toothed disc. The disc can be seen in Plate 24. A wheel in the clock with a pin in it was arranged to rotate once in 24 hours and, between 10 and midnight, the date was advanced by the pin pushing a tooth of the calendar wheel. To make the calendar wheel flick over, a 'jumper' was provided, i.e. a spring which pressed between the teeth to make the wheel click from one position to the next. The calendar wheel is held while being operated by the clock but is free at other times.

Such calendar mechanisms are set by reaching behind the dial and turning the wheel by hand, or by turning from the front with the aid of a small pin if little holes or indentations are provided by the numbers. There is no automatic correction for months shorter than 31 days so on these occasions the dial must be turned on to 1 by hand.

A hand moving round a small dial marked from 1 to 31 was an alternative arrangement, (Plate 17) or a long hand concentric with the minute hand moving around the normal dial which was marked outside or inside the hour circle with 31 divisions (Plate 58). Such a hand is operated in the same way by being attached to a toothed wheel identical to the toothed calendar disc.

Calendars that are automatically correct at the end of each month so that adjustment by hand is unnecessary are called 'annual calendars'. They are found on clocks made after about 1700 and particularly on clocks of French origin from the eighteenth and nineteenth centuries. An annual calendar normally has every month and date of the year marked round the perimeter of the main dial or a subsidiary dial that rotates once in a year and is in effect attached to a 365-toothed wheel. In leap years, the hand has to be retarded by hand a day after February 28 (Plates 5 and 74).

Occasionally a clock was fitted with a perpetual calendar, i.e. one that automatically corrected for leap years. The best known type was on French clocks made by Brocot (1817–78). This had three calendar dials plus a moon dial, all operated by a mechanism itself worked from a single lever operated from the clock. The calendar dials showed the day of the week, the month, and the date. On some clocks a fourth hand showed whether it was a leap year or not.

Very occasionally English clocks of the eighteenth century were made with perpetual calendars, but they usually had various other complications as well, having been constructed to special order or as a *tour de force* of the maker.

A perpetual calendar has to have one wheel in its mechanism that causes a change once in four years, just as one accurate over a non-leap year has to have a 'year wheel', and one accurate over a 31-day month, a 'month wheel'.

Church feasts were more important centuries ago than they are today in the life of the people, and clocks occasionally were made to indicate them on their calendar dials. The Dominical Letter was also indicated, a letter from A to G from which the dates of Sundays throughout the year, or the date on which a particular day of the week would fall, could be discovered by reference to a table printed in earlier versions of prayer books. Dominical Letters were shown by nearly all astronomical clocks of the Renaissance period. They appeared on an occasional complicated longcase clock made in England in the later eighteenth century (Plate 72).

The Golden Number, also indicated by some such clocks, was provided in order to help calculate the movable feast of Easter. The number is related to the cycle of new and full moons which repeats itself over a period of nineteen years, as discovered by the Athenian astronomer, Meton, and named the 'Metonic cycle'. The number is calculated by adding together the digits of the year, adding one, and dividing by 19. Thus the digits of 1967 added equal 23, plus 1 equals 24. Divide by 19 and there is a remainder of 5, which is the Golden Number, so called because it was carved in stone and gilded in Greek temples.

MOON DIALS

Many eighteenth and early nineteenth century clocks have moon dials. The moon dial was particularly practical in days when street lighting was non-existent and lanterns not very effective out of doors, because the traveller had to depend upon the light of the moon. There were also a number of superstitious practices that depended upon the moon. For example, in some parts it was thought unwise to fasten shingles to roofs when the moon's horns turned up because the ends of the shingles would do likewise. Also planting times were related by some farmers to the moon, as seeds were expected to germinate more rapidly when the moon was waxing. Recent research indicates some foundation in this second belief. There is also evidence to indicate that biting times of fish is correlated with the moon, and that the weather is affected by it, the driest days occurring two or three days before new or full moon and the wettest days two or three days after.

Moon dials, showing the phase and age of the moon, appeared in the early sixteenth century on clocks in order to avoid the inconvenience of having to look up tables in an almanac. They became common during the eighteenth, particularly on English longcase clocks. The moon dials of early European clocks comprised two discs in the centre of the main dial. The outer disc had an eccentric circular

I

hole in it and the inner one was painted with a black circle, the same size as the hole, placed eccentrically on a white ground. The discs were bosses of the solar and lunar hands and rotated at different rates so that the appearance of the moon was shown through the hole.

A simpler scheme was incorporated in English longcase clocks from after about the first quarter of the eighteenth century. They copied the almanacs of the time, which showed ● for a new moon (i.e. no moon) and ○ for a full moon. In the dial was a circular aperture and behind this a disc painted with a black man-in-the-moon face to represent the new moon (Plate 73) and a white man-in-the-moon face to represent the full moon. This disc was rotated once in 29½ days, which is approximately one lunation. A true lunation is 29 days 12 hr. 44 min. 2.8 sec., so the moon dial was only half a day out over a year.

There were scenes or stars painted or engraved between the moon faces. As the disc was rotated, part of a face as seen through the circular aperture would gradually appear or disappear to show the phases of the moon. Because no moon was represented by a dark face in the dial, this may be confusing at first to a present-day owner, but the age of the moon is almost always indicated also around the edge of the disc, and shown through a small separate aperture. The age is shown in days from 1 to 29½.

The moon dial was operated in the same way as the calendar, by saw-shaped teeth on its edge, stepped forwards by a pin on one of the clock wheels. It is obviously impossible to cut 29½ teeth. Clockmakers neatly side-stepped the problem by cutting twice that number, 59, and stepping the wheel round every 12 hours instead of every 24 hours.

The next type of moon dial was similar, except that both moon faces were painted white to represent full moons and the moon dial was rotated once during the two lunations. Each face represented a full moon and the space between them no moon, i.e. new moon.

A similar arrangement was used with the break-arch dial. It showed the quarters of the moon the correct shape, however, unlike the moon dials just described. A similar disc was employed with two faces of the moon on it, both white and similar to each other so that each indicated a full moon. This dial was turned once in 59 days.

Instead of a circular aperture to show the moons, there was the arrangement as shown in Plate 16, so that a moon face moving through a semi-circle in a clockwise direction would first indicate a thin crescent with the horns down, gradually increase to full at the top of its travel, then decrease with the horns down. The age of the moon was shown by days engraved or painted round the edge of the disc and indicating against a pointer at the top. The second face began to appear as the first disappeared, of course, and the short time while they were both hidden behind the semi-circular pieces of the aperture indicated the new moon.

On all these types of moon dial, a correction of half a day losing should be made yearly by moving the disc back a tooth.

An early form of moon dial on continental clocks that was also incorporated on a few of the first longcase clocks and came into favour again later on in Yorkshire, in particular during the second half of the eighteenth century, was a rotating ball. The ball was half black and half silvered or white. When it showed black to the front, it indicated a new moon, and white a full moon, the intermediate positions being the quarters. It was usually positioned in the dial arch and had a numbered band indicating the age. Operation was by a gear-driven shaft. A common name for the indication is a 'Halifax moon', after the place where makers were particularly fond of it.

Knowing the phase of the moon was only a part of knowing when it would be light enough to venture out; there were dangers from footpads and highwaymen as well as obstacles. The next information required was the time of rising and setting of the moon. The indication was complicated to achieve on a clock and was only rarely done. One is shown in Plate 72. Very infrequently a clock was made with a more accurate moon train. Renaissance clocks from Europe frequently showed the moon's position in the zodiac in relation to the sun.

Time of sunrise and sunset were provided by a few complicated clocks, again like that in Plate 72.

TIDAL DIALS

The first Astronomer Royal in England, John Flamsteed, measured the state of the tide of the Thames at London Bridge and published the figures, which were invaluable to shipping coming up the river as well as to local shipping on which so much transport depended. Isaac Newton became interested and discovered that the time of the tide depended upon the moon. Thomas Tompion, the most famous of English clockmakers, made two longcase clocks about 1675 which showed the time of the tide at London Bridge, but very few clockmakers followed suit, as far as is known, until the astronomer, James Ferguson, who wrote popular scientific books at the time, described in simple language how tides occurred and also designed a tidal dial for manual operation which he later had incorporated in a clock. Several clockmakers copied this; it showed a blue-coloured plate representing water between two rocks. The plate rose and fell with the tides, being operated by a cam driven by the clock.

In the last quarter of the eighteenth century, tidal dials on longcase clocks became quite popular with provincial makers in England especially in areas that depended upon water transport. An earlier version is seen in Plate 16. Many were made in the west country. Some of these dials were made for local conditions and others were universal, being adjustable for any part of the country.

During one lunation of 29½ days, the time of high tide anywhere changes gradually until at the end of the period it is 24 hours later. If, therefore, an age-of-moon dial is calibrated into 24 hours also, it will show a time about 48 minutes less every day, which is the amount by which high tide changes. If this scale of 24 hours is correct for local high tide when the moon is full, it will continue to give correct indications at all other times.

Tidal clocks made only for one locality had the hours engraved appropriately around the age-of-moon dial. But some clockmakers made a separate ring of hour numerals and attached it friction tight to the age-of-moon dial. This made it possible to advance or retard it to suit any locality. If high tide were at 2 p.m. in one place at full moon (i.e. at 14¾ days' age of the moon), the hour ring could be moved round to, say, 2.45 p.m. to adjust it for another place.

In most places there are two tides a day. The other time was arrived at by subtracting 24 minutes.

The tidal dial was often separate from the age of moon indication, but on some clocks, one hand indicated both age of the moon and the time of one high tide. The tidal hours were normally marked I to XII repeated, instead of I to XXIIII.

EQUATION DIALS

Before describing the next indication, it is necessary to say something about time of day as measured by a clock. Today few people query the regularity of time or the invariable length of the day because we have a universal time system, but it was not always so and the fact that days are in fact of different lengths was brought to light by clocks.

The days, as measured by sundials, are not of equal length throughout the year. This is because the Earth's orbit is an ellipse, and the Sun is at one of the foci. A day is measured by the interval from the sun at its meridian (its highest point in the sky) on one day to its meridian on the next, and these apparent solar days vary in length through the year. But clocks keep to mean time – a steady average rate – so the sundial is about 16 minutes fast of the clock in November, for example, which partially explains why it gets dark so early in November. It was very important to know the difference between sundial time and clock time before time signals, because the only way of setting a clock to time was by comparing it with a sundial. Consequently if people with clocks set them to time by sundials on different days of the year, the clocks would show different times. The difference is appreciable – from 14 minutes slow to 16 minutes fast, a half-hour variation – and is known as the 'equation of time'.

When a customer bought a reliable clock in the eighteenth century and earlier, he would probably have a sundial delivered with it. After the later seventeenth century he would also have a table of figures giving the equation of time for different days of the year. To set his clock, he would read the sundial at noon, refer to the tables to see how many minutes he was to add or subtract, then set his clock accordingly.

To remind the owner of the equation of time, some early clocks had a movable ring marked in hours fitted over a fixed one marked similarly. The movable ring was set by hand according to the tables. The next system was an annual calendar with the equation of time engraved on it (Plate 74).

Near the end of the seventeenth century, Christiaan Huygens realized that the clock itself could indicate the equation of time automatically and he or someone else devised a cam, called an 'equation kidney' because of its shape, which rotated once a year and moved a lever pressing on its edge. The lever turned an indicating disc or a hand backwards or forwards to show the difference between clock and sundial time.

Later equation clocks had a scale marked in minutes in the dial arch as shown in Plate 75. Zero was in the middle and minutes fast and minutes slow were indicated by the position of the hand. A more sophisticated arrangement also came into use showing actual sundial time, not just the equation of time. It needed differential gearing, invented by the clockmaker Joseph Williamson, and a long time later applied to the back axles of motor-cars. Extra hour and minute hands showed sundial time on a separate dial, or there was just a separate minute hand, concentric with the normal clock minute hand, which ran fast or slow of the normal minute hand according to the equation of time. A watch with an equation dial of this type is shown in Plate 97.

SIDEREAL TIME

Still another complication of time is that used by astronomers and known as 'sidereal time'. It was shown by some special clocks instead of mean solar time, i.e. equal hours. Some clocks indicated both sidereal time and mean time on separate dials (Plate 43).

Sidereal time is time measured from a fixed or 'clock' star instead of the sun. Sidereal hours are of equal length, but are shorter than the hours of mean time. Sidereal time, although accurate, is impractical for daily use as it ignores the periods of daylight and darkness, giving a day of 23 hours, 56 minutes and 4.1 seconds. In practice today, astronomers measure the time of rotation of the Earth from a clock star, make certain corrections to this time, and distribute it by means of time signals for people to set their clocks.

We are used now to having uniform time all over the country, but this was not always so. Noon is defined as the time when the sun is at its meridian, i.e. its highest point in the sky. As the sun 'moves' from east to west, it is noon sooner in eastern parts of the country than in western parts. When people set their clocks by sundials, clocks indicated local time, so that someone travelling with a clock set to time in London would find it fast if he checked it with a clock set to time in Bristol, to the west. This did not matter when people were born, lived and died in a village without much outside contact, although it was inconvenient when travelling by coach, so coaches carried and worked by their own time. (See Plate 37.) On the other hand, the pace of living was slower and travellers would allow themselves a day to catch the coach for London, whereas today they allow themselves half a minute to catch the train.

When railways began to spread over the country in the early nineteenth century, the use of local times became very inconvenient. It was obviously almost impossible to work a railway using local times, so the railway companies used their own 'railway time', which was controlled by their central depots. They used this to calculate their timetables and there were some bad collisions on lines used jointly by different railway companies who based their timetables on different 'railway times'. The railways eventually got together and agreed to use centralized company time, actually that of the Great Western Railway at Swindon.

In 1880, Greenwich Mean Time was established by law as official time all over Britain, and accepted by the railways. In 1884, it was adopted by the rest of the world at an international conference (only France and Ireland voting against it) as a basis of time zones. The world was divided into 24 time zones of 15 degrees of longitude each. The longitude at Greenwich was considered zero and zones westwards became successively one hour earlier and zones eastwards successively one hour later.

WORLD TIME DIALS

Occasionally a clock is seen with a world time dial (Plate 72). This is easily understood by imagining oneself standing on the north pole. The sun would be shining from a certain direction and places underneath it would be at noon. On the opposite side of the world it would be midnight, so all the 24 hours could be marked round you. The centre of a world time clock represents the north pole, and around it are engraved or painted the names of some of the world's most important towns. A dial engraved with the hours from 1 to 24 rotates against the place-names. This principle was understood from the earliest days of clocks, but world time clocks were more commonly made in the later eighteenth century and showed local times in towns elsewhere in the world.

ASTRONOMICAL DIALS

The zodiac is an imaginary belt in the heavens to which all fixed stars are confined and it is divided into 12 signs of 30 degrees each. Even in the fourteenth century, clocks were being made to show the position of the sun in the zodiac; some had another hand to show the moon's position in the zodiac also. This was considered valuable information at a time when communities were ruled by believers in astrology.

In later years, clocks were occasionally made to operate planetaria, showing the actual movements of the individual planets around the sun, but the collector is not likely to come across one of these. He is more likely to see one operating a planisphere or star map. Long-case clocks with them were constructed occasionally in the later eighteenth century.

In the lower part of the dial, usually, was an oval opening behind which a star map was rotated by the clock. Plate 72 shows one above the dial. The part visible showed the night sky at that particular time of the year. Such a clock was, of course, made for a particular latitude.

14 Watches

THE invention of the mainspring made the portable clock possible. The personal portable clock – the watch – followed soon after. There are references in the later fifteenth century to small clocks that could be moved about but no certain reference to a watch before 1500. The watch, worn on a cord around the neck or attached, perhaps with a bunch of keys, to the belt, was invented in Europe but where it is not certain. It might have been in Italy, France, or southern Germany.

The first watches were probably spherical in shape. A record of 1511 refers to those made by Peter Henlein of Nuremberg carried on the breast or in the purse. The iron movements were mounted in musk balls. The musk ball was a metal sphere, decorated and perforated, in which musk was placed. It was worn as scent is today.

A French watch of the musk-ball type, made in 1551 by Jacques de la Garde of Blois, can be seen in the Louvre in Paris and there is also a German watch of the type. The dial looks like a small base to the ball. There is a single hand and no cover. Opposite it is a loop for hanging from a chain.

These watches are wrongly called 'Nuremberg eggs' owing to a translator mistaking *Ueurlein* (little clocks) in 1730 for *Eierlein* (little eggs), a mistake that has been copied ever since.

Blois in France and Nuremberg in Germany were two of the first early watchmaking centres. The Italian industry is not so well documented, although it certainly existed at a very early date. The French industry grew rapidly, expanding to Paris, Lyon, Rouen, Dijon, Sedan, Grenoble, and elsewhere. French watchmakers were the best from the start, and in the first quarter of the seventeenth century they dominated particularly, mainly because the Thirty Years' War sapped German economic strength. The English industry lagged far behind the rest, although there were a few watchmakers at work in London.

137

Watchmaking was from its earliest days an international trade and apprentices were trained in one of the early centres mentioned – Paris was a very active one – or in Geneva or London, where centres had also grown up. After apprenticeship they became journeymen, and would return to their home towns or join watchmakers in other centres. Some would specialize in one or another aspect of the work, making watch mechanisms or their parts in series for sale to other watchmakers. This exchange went on between different workshops in the same and different cities, even between different countries.

The division of work was particularly marked in watchmaking because several earlier crafts were involved, particularly that of the goldsmith. By mid-seventeenth century there were separate crafts of watchmaker, goldsmith, jeweller, engraver, enameller, and lapidary casemaker (maker of rock crystal cases) at least – all concerned with producing watches.

Batch production methods were also employed by goldsmiths and jewellers for watch cases. Separate craft guilds controlled different trades, which led to disputes, despite the close-working co-operation. For example, in London the Worshipful Company of Goldsmiths claimed the right in the second half of the seventeenth century to search watchmakers' and clockmakers' premises in order to test their gold for purity.

One of the reasons for internationalism was religious intolerance, because Blois was one centre of the Huguenot (French protestant) religion and on the revocation of the Edict of Nantes in 1685 many Huguenot watchmakers followed those who had already gone from Paris and other centres to England or crossed the mountains into Switzerland, where they were not persecuted for their beliefs.

The watch and/or clockmaker of the time was usually also the retailer. He made some parts, bought others, designed and assembled the movement, bought a case and engraved his name and town on the movement and sold the whole watch to a customer. Owing to all these factors, the productions of the different watchmaking countries in the seventeenth century were very similar, and a London watch, for example, might well bear the name of a French watchmaker. The town name on the watch is often the only certain indication of where it was finished.

London's watchmaking industry got into its stride about 1600 or just after and became dominant at the end of the century.

Perhaps contemporary with musk-ball watches were purse-sized versions of drum-shaped table clocks, which by their shape were truer progenitors of the watch. Nearly all German sixteenth-century watches were more accurately clock-watches, since they struck the hours. They were heavily decorated by engraving all over the brass dial. The case was pierced, to allow the striking to be heard, and engraved front and back and round the straight sides. The cover or lid of the case was hinged so that it could be opened to expose the dial (Plate 76).

There was a single stubby hour hand which could be turned by the fingers for setting. It indicated the time on a dial with a silver chapter ring marked in hours and half-hours. The cover was pierced so that the position of the hand could be seen without having to open the cover. Small knobs at the hour chapters enabled the time to be found by touch with the cover open at night, 12 being at the hinge position.

The dials of early German watches, spherical, drum-shaped, and rounded as in Plate 76, had an outer ring of hour numerals from I to XII with an inner ring in Arabic numerals from 13 to 24 to suit the 24 system of timekeeping then in vogue. The covers of these had pairs of holes for the numerals to be seen. Sixteenth-century German watches had the 2 in the Arabic numbers engraved like a Z.

The movements of these watches were hinged in the case so that they could be raised to expose the backplate. This practice continued into the eighteenth century. They had no glasses but covers were at times made of rock crystal.

Towards the end of the sixteenth century, the French began making oval-shaped watches, the sides of which were still like the drum watch, but which had slightly dome-shaped back and cover, the whole watch being elaborately engraved (Plate 77). About the same time, the sides of watches were given a convex shape until the oval watch with curved sides became the most typical of the early seventeenth century (Plate 78).

FORM WATCHES

As watchmakers became more venturesome, watches became more varied and the long octagon shape became popular. Sometimes the cover was made of faceted rock crystal so that the time indication and decoration inside could be better seen. In the second half of the seventeenth century many novel shapes, some in crystal, which are now known as 'form watches', were introduced. They included faceted ovals; cruciform, shaped like a cross; books; skulls; birds or animals; and flowers, particularly the tulip (Plate 79).

Cutting rock crystal cases may have been a speciality of Geneva. Incidentally, the laws of the Guild of Goldsmiths of Geneva of 1566 forbade the making of crosses, false stones, hollow rings, and 'other instruments serving popery'; but later, rock crystal crosses were the town's speciality and were known as 'abbess watches'.

Brass was the main material for the framework of cases during the first half of the seventeenth century, but silver covers and sides gave them an all-silver appearance. Cheaper productions were all brass.

As a centre of case-making, Blois supplied other countries with its products. Many so-called English cases of the early seventeenth century were probably made in Blois because they were almost identical with similarly-dated French watches. Moreover, cases 'made' in the provinces were of equal quality to those made in London, which reinforces the argument.

Similarity of decoration came from the use of pattern books by craftsmen, a practice common through the ages. Hogarth, for example, drew patterns for jewellers, and Chippendale, Sheraton, and Adam, for furniture makers. Perhaps the most popular pattern books for watch case makers of the early seventeenth century were those of ornamentation for locksmiths, sword hilts, and watches by Antoine Jacquard of Poitiers, who favoured many human figures, often in erotic positions.

Despite the internationalism of design, English watches sometimes had one distinguishing feature, an engraved border around the back plate (Plate 80) and around the dial. Also, English makers favoured a tall italic script for their names, engraved on the back plate.

Before the mid-seventeenth century, when circular cases were displacing oval ones, there was also a change in ornamentation of engraved cases from small human figures to tulips and fritillary (a lily type of plant) as with the engraved dials and back plates of clocks.

DECORATION

The most colourful watches were those decorated in enamels. Enamelling had been practised in Europe well before the invention of the watch and flourished as a trade in France (Limoges), Germany (Mosam), Holland and Switzerland. The English also produced some fine enamelled gold cases during the first half of the seven-teenth century until the end of the eighteenth. Enamelling is so important a decoration during this period that it is dealt with separately, in Chapter 15. An example of Blois enamelling by the Huaud brothers, the well-known enamellers, is shown in Plate 81.

Decoration was not confined to the case. Movements were elabo-rately engraved on the back plate. The balance cock – the separate piece which carries one of the bearings for the balance – was heavily decorated by piercing and carving. Balance cocks (or bridges) fol-lowed a sequence in development from the first simple S-shape to a pierced oval with pierced foot. The foot was openwork of irregular shape or oval like the table of the cock, and the pattern was based on foliage (Plates 77 and 80).

By about the mid-seventeenth century, the cock became round in shape and very much bigger, so did bridges on French watches. The circular cock with a rim edge was of the same diameter as the balance. Large cocks, the earliest of the period, became smaller as the century progressed. With these changes, the foot of the balance also lost its irregular outline and in the last quarter was usually wedge-shaped with the outer edge curved to follow the circular edge of the movement. Circular balance cocks had symmetrical patterns (Plate 82), as a rule, until nearly the mid-eighteenth century when asym-metrical ones became popular. Later, balance cocks became tapered and narrower (Plates 90 and 108).

The pillars of a watch movement that separate the plates can help in dating, although shapes appeared and disappeared with fashion changes. The first pillars were of simple baluster form, like those of clocks. After about 1650, makers introduced a variety of shapes, one of which was the tulip pillar, an extremely popular pattern with craftsmen and artists of all kinds during the second half of the seven-teenth century. At about the end of the century, a tapered 'Egyptian' pillar came into favour. In the meantime, plainer square baluster pillars still appeared in watches made at almost all times. (Fig. 24).

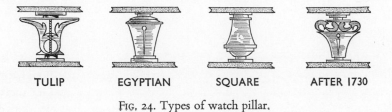

TULIP   EGYPTIAN   SQUARE   AFTER 1730

FIG. 24. Types of watch pillar.

Despite the early addiction to ornamentation, there appeared a number of very plain watches well before the second half of the seventeenth century in England. They were of small, oval – almost flattened egg shape – and in a plain silver case without any decoration, or some simple engraving, like the watch in Plate 78. The dial was silver with a steel hand covered by a glass. The movement, however, had the usual elaborately pierced balance cock. They are known as 'Puritan watches'.

PENDANTS

Pendants, from which the watch was hung or attached to a chain, were at first circular rings. The ring passed loosely through another ring or a knop on the side of the case (Plate 78). The loose ring was 'fore and aft' when the watch was intended for hanging from a cord round the neck, but it gradually became more usual to drill the knop from side to side. Later in its history, the knop had a long stem attaching it to the inner case, to allow for the pair case and also the outer protective case, and the ring became a bow hinged at each side of the knop (Plate 81). Towards the end of the eighteenth century, bows had become flatter and more oval in shape, but still on long stems (Plate 86).

When the pair case, described on the next page, was superseded by the single case in the nineteenth century, knops without stems were again attached to outer cases, and had circular, or ring, bows. Pump-winding watches (described in Chapter 16) had this type of pendant, the 'pump' being the top of the knop. The pendant eventually became combined with the winding button of the keyless pocket watch of the later nineteenth century.

An enamelled watch was sometimes carried by its bow on a chatelaine, the chain holding the keys worn by the mistress of a medieval castle. The chatelaine was beautified by gold work and decorated enamel and trinkets instead of keys were attached with the watch (Plate 83). The chatelaine watch was popular in Georgian and Victorian times.

POCKET WATCHES

In the last quarter of the seventeenth century, two inventions had a profound influence on watches. One was the balance spring, which improved accuracy considerably, and the other the waistcoat which provided a convenient place to carry the watch. The earlier Puritan fashion of concealing a watch in a pocket now became the fashion. As the watch disappeared from view around the neck, so customers for watches became less insistent on decoration. Moreover, a larger, and therefore more accurate watch was more easily carried in a waistcoat pocket, which encouraged the making of lower-priced, larger watches. Nevertheless, the gaudy ornamental watch still had a strong following until the 1800s.

The biggest change with the balance spring was the rapid introduction of two hands – hour and minute – and of better means of regulation. Watches tended to become thicker.

Carved and engraved landscapes and groups of figures began to disappear and floral patterns, usually incorporating birds and animals, took their place. The new designs were usually in repoussé, a raised decoration carried out from the back (Plate 84). Repoussé cases were at first in simple patterns, then became elaborate during the first quarter of the eighteenth century. They reached their peak of popularity between 1725 and 1750. A quarter of a century later they had gone almost completely out of favour.

After about 1700 the watch remained very much the same in appearance, with its verge movement with balance and spring, and its decorated metal repoussé, or enamelled, outer case and dial, until about 1750. It was a time when English makers took the lead from the French. Later in the century, it was the turn of the French again to lead in fashion and output, although the English still provided most technical improvements. The watch in Plate 85 is typical in shape although it is an unusual watch, being a complicated one by Thomas Mudge, with grande sonnerie and minute repeating, of 1757.

PAIR CASES

About 1675, the pair case was introduced, an arrangement that separated even more the work of the casemaker and the watchmaker. The watch movement was hinged into a plain case of silver or gold. This fitted snugly into the separate outer case which was decorated by repoussé, or other treatment, and had a hole the same size as the glass of the dial. As many pair cases were works of art and needed protection, a third case was sometimes provided to enclose the pair case (Plate 86). This was more rugged, but nevertheless still decorative. Leather covering was commonly used, studded with gold or silver pins in a decorative design known as piqué. The leather was at times treated and dyed green and at other times rough fish skin was used. A third decorative treatment for protective cases was tortoise-shell inlaid with silver.

From about 1725, many movements were fitted with gilded brass dust caps held in place by a spring catch. A late one is shown in Plate 103.

During the second half of the eighteenth and the first quarter of the nineteenth centuries, the pocket watch changed considerably in appearance. With Breguet as their pace-setter, the French abandoned their method of winding through the dial. Instead, the movement was fitted into a ring around its edge. The glass was in a bezel hinged to the front. The back held an inner hinged lid, with winding holes through it, and an outer lid forming the back of the case.

Although the French led the fashion for thinner and plainer watches, the English continued to make pair cases from about mid-eighteenth century and into the first quarter of the nineteenth. Later ones were not truly pair cases, although they appear to be, because the parts are not separate but fixed together. Plate 89 shows a French case of this type.

Many better watches of this time had cases of undecorated gold or silver, but during the last quarter of the century engine-turning was favoured, often of simple barleycorn pattern. Enamelling, when used, was often confined to an inset panel. Both French and Swiss continued to be expert at this craft. A favourite decoration of the last quarter of the eighteenth century was to surround the enamelling on the back of the case, and the dial, with a circle of half-round pearls (Plate 87). Around 1800 transparent enamel was used over engine-turning.

Some later eighteenth-century English watches had painted cases covered with a transparent layer of horn which, although apparently produced for customers who could not afford the best, were attractive.

Continental watches had very narrow bezels around the glass. Also the glasses themselves were flatter. On fine work, the 'glass' was sometimes cut from rock crystal, reverting to an earlier practice.

SELF-WINDING

Towards the end of the eighteenth century the first self-winding

144

pocket watches appeared. They were called 'pedometer watches' because an oscillating weight like that in pedometers was responsible for winding the mainspring as the wearer moved. A Swiss version produced in some quantity in the 1890s is shown in Plate 88. Invented about the same time, was a self-winding watch with a rotating weight. One is shown in Plate 89.

During the eighteenth century and into the nineteenth, Swiss watchmakers had been making steady progress and built up big export markets for their watches. Their chief competitors were the French, for whom Japy pioneered machine-made watches, and the English, who concentrated on much plainer watches which were good timekeepers. The Swiss went for decoration and novelty. When the competition among them depended on which would adopt mechanical methods of production, it was the French and the Swiss who succeeded.

LEVER WATCHES

Fine English watches were made and exported in large quantities in the nineteenth century but have not up to now acquired the same collector value as Swiss ones because they were less decorative, although often in precious metal cases. The English adopted the 'forked escapement', later known as the 'lever', invented by Thomas Mudge for watches in 1770, but not used generally in England until it was redeveloped through the efforts of Josiah Emery, and later particularly of the Lancashire maker Peter Litherland, for cheaper watches (Plate 90). By 1850, however, it was established as the best also for quality work, and the English lever pocket watch with fusee movement became the *sine qua non* of personal timekeepers, remaining so until the Swiss machine-made watch began to oust it in the later nineteenth century.

A large number of English watches of the early nineteenth century were converted to lever escapement from duplex or perhaps cylinder, so what appears an early lever watch should always be regarded with suspicion until it is proved to be so.

LATE WATCHES

Although the Swiss made most progress eventually in watch production, the French, followed by the Americans, were the first to apply machine methods and a few of their early machine-made watches designed for cheapness have achieved collector status because of their ingenuity and their present rarity. One is the Waterbury watch, invented by Daniel Buck and made by the Waterbury Watch Co. in America, from 1880 to 1898. The firm continued as the New England Watch Co. until 1912. The watch was known as the 'old long wind Waterbury' because its mainspring was between eight and nine feet long. It was a form of tourbillon (described in Chapter 16) in which, however, the *whole movement* revolved in the case, following a patent of a few years earlier, the Auburndale watch, which proved unsuccessful.

All parts of the Waterbury were hand-stamped from sheet metal instead of being hand-finished like the English and Swiss watches of the period. It consisted of only 58 parts including screws and case. The movement revolved once an hour around a stationary centre wheel attached to the case and had a simplified duplex escapement. Hands were set by pushing them round. Many types of Waterbury watches were made. Another early American watch, produced for cheapness from 1892, but now a collector's piece, was the 'dollar watch', made by Ingersoll. One is shown in Plate 91.

The earliest Swiss version of a cheap watch was the Roscopf, invented by a German of that name and made between 1865 and 1867. It had an ingeniously simplified movement which reverted to

FIG. 25. The first 'Railway watch', by Roscopf.

the very earliest in layout, but incorporated a number of ideas including the pin pallet escapement, used in cheap wrist watches of today. The hands were set, however, by pushing them round after opening the hinged bezel of the glass. The early Roscopf was taken up particularly by Belgian railways for their employees and was the first to be known as a 'railway watch'. (Fig. 25.)

RING AND MINIATURE WATCHES

The idea of setting a small watch in a ring is surprisingly ancient. The Duke of Urbino had a clock watch mounted in a ring in 1542. In 1764, John Arnold made a small ring watch which was a quarter repeater with 120 parts and a movement only ⅜ in. across. It had the first known ruby cylinder escapement. It probably still exists although its whereabouts are unknown, although there is a ring watch in the Usher collection at Lincoln said to be this one.

At many periods, watchmakers tried to express their skill by producing miniature watches and this became an industry in Switzerland in the nineteenth century. Many were set in rings (the French one shown in Plate 92 also has a calendar dial), others in seals, miniature vases, and balls. Many were fitted into miniature version of pocket watch cases with key wind (Plate 93). Even automata watches were made small enough to be set in rings.

WRIST WATCHES

The idea of wearing a small watch on a band around the wrist occurred at an early date. Queen Elizabeth I had one and there are several examples of the seventeenth century. The Empress Josephine had a wrist watch with a gold and pearl bracelet made in 1806 and Swiss makers fitted some of their miniature pocket watches into bracelets or attached them to velvet wrist bands from about 1850. The wrist watch with a leather strap was possibly invented by E. A. Pearson, a London saddler, just before the first world war, the watch at first being held in a leather cup. Later, wire lugs to which the halves of the straps were sewn were soldered to the sides of the case (Plate 94).

Perhaps one recent wrist watch could be added to a list of watches with collector potential. It is the first self-winding wrist watch, invented and made by an Englishman, John Harwood, between 1928 and 1932. Harwood watches have no winding buttons. The hands are set by turning the bezel of the glass in one direction or the other. One is shown in Plate 94.

15 *Watch Dials and Decorations*

WATCH DIALS AND HANDS

BEFORE the balance spring was introduced towards the end of the seventeenth century, dials were engraved and the engraved lines filled with a black wax, and there was a single hour hand. The balance and spring accuracy encouraged the addition of a minute hand, with dials divided into 60 minutes as well as the hours and quarters. Clock practice was followed, marking the hours in Roman numerals and every five minutes in large Arabic numerals, as shown in Plate 89.

The method of applying a coating of silver to another metal – silvering – used for watch and clock dials, was introduced about 1660. Before that, and afterwards for watches, real silver was sometimes employed for the dial. Silvered dials had the numerals on another piece of metal separately applied.

About the same time as the balance spring's introduction, towards the end of the seventeenth century, a fashion started for champlevé dials in England, and this continued into the eighteenth century. In France and Switzerland many watches were being made with dials similar to their clocks, that is with separate enamel plaques bearing the hour numerals (Plate 95). Sometimes the entire dial was enamelled with raised portions for the chapters, although they were not particularly suitable for watches with a minute hand which stretched over the chapters. This obstacle encouraged the use of smooth enamelled dials, usually opaque white with black numerals.

The plain white enamelled dial (Plate 85) was popular with makers of all countries by 1750, although some continued to use engraved precious metal for about another quarter of a century. Pictorial, coloured enamel dials never lost favour and were made in varying numbers at all times. The plain white dials had black Roman hours and Arabic minute figures, but the minute figures began to disappear in the late eighteenth century, leaving Roman hour chapters only

(Plate 99). Before the nineteenth century, some watches had Arabic hours (Plate 92).

Towards the end of the eighteenth century, Breguet reintroduced the gold dial, but decorated it with a fine pattern of engine-turning which, of course, produced geometrical patterns (Plate 99).

COMPLEX DIALS

As with early clocks, early watches sometimes were much more complex than later ones, incorporating moon dials and calendar work, sometimes showing the day of the week as well as the month. Signs of the zodiac and even the seasons of the year were indicated by some. Astronomical watches of this period showed some indications by hands and others by rotating discs showing through sector-shaped openings in the main dial.

At that critical time for watches, around 1700, before dials became more or less standardized in the form we now know, there were some interesting attempts to make watches easier to read. People were not then 'broken in' as children to reading a dial. One experiment was the six-hour dial which had a circle of Roman numerals from I to VI and a circle of Arabic ones from 7 to 12. The single hand rotated once in six hours and the time was read off the Roman or Arabic numerals according to whether it was morning or afternoon. The purpose was to make it easier to read minutes because of the faster moving hand. There was also the 24 hours dial referred to on page 139.

Another experiment, the wandering hour dial, probably owed its origin to the night clocks of the period described in Chapter 8. A Roman numeral moves through a semi-circle marked from 0 to 60 minutes, as shown in Plate 45. When one hour disappears to the right, the next appears at the left. Thus hours and minutes were indicated without the use of a hand.

A third variation was the sun and moon watch. The hours are marked VI, VII, VIII, IX, X, XI, XII, I, II, III, IV, V, VI, around the curve of a semi-circular opening in the dial. During the day, a picture of the sun moves round the semi-circle to indicate the hour. It is followed by a picture of the moon moving under the night hours. Minutes are indicated by a normal hand indicating on an outer ring of minutes.

There were a few other, now very rare, arrangements. Watches sometimes had dials that followed the regulator system of using a centre seconds hand, and separate hour and minute hands one above the other indicating on separate circles of numbers.

PENDULUM WATCH

An oddity of the period around 1700, when the accuracy of the pendulum on clocks made such an impression, was the 'pendulum watch'. Actually a pendulum will not work on a watch, but some makers located the balance wheel under the dial, which had a curved slot in it. A small disc fixed on the balance rim could be seen swinging in the slot, like the mock pendulum of the bracket clock in the Frontispiece. The Dutch had a similar system on some of their watches, but the balance was left in the usual place on the back plate, so the case had to be opened to see it.

WATCH HANDS

Hands at the early period were made of steel and were thick and stubby with longish tails. Enamelled watches often had hands of gilt. Two hands on watches were most commonly of what is known as 'beetle and poker' shape, as shown in Plate 85, although sometimes makers used designs similar to clock hands of the time. An hour hand with an arrow-head was also employed, but towards the end of the eighteenth century the heart shape and the spade hand, which is in fact similar to the heart, came into favour. Breguet preferred matching hands with circular holes (Plate 99) and many makers followed suit in the nineteenth century. These are also known as 'moon hands' because the eccentric centre hole left a crescent shape. The heart-shaped hand was sometimes pierced also. (See Fig. 3, Nos. 23 to 27.)

GLASSES

There is no certainty about the date of the introduction of watch glasses, but it was some time towards mid-seventeenth century. Until then a hinged cover was fitted over the dial and it was quite common to set in it a shaped piece of rock crystal, held by tags, or in later versions by a split bezel. In place of rock crystal, some watches had glasses made by blowing a bulb and cutting a disc from it, which caused certain early glasses to be rather bulbous. At first these were held in place in the same way as the rock crystal; then, as the end of the century approached, it was found unnecessary to make the bezel with a split as the glass was sufficiently elastic for it to be sprung into a solid groove of slightly smaller diameter in a bezel hinged to the case. As a matter of interest, watch glasses are still called 'crystals' on the continent today.

COMPLICATED WATCHES

Complicated watches were made from the earliest times, as were complicated clocks, astronomical indications then having been of some importance to the watch owner. Some had dial indications referred to in Chapter 13 and mechanisms were in principle the same as those described in the clock section of this book.

The English maker, Daniel Quare, won a patent for a repeating watch in 1687. (A more involved one was devised at the same time by Edward Barlow who invented rack striking for clocks.) A button was pressed and the last hour was sounded on a bell in the back of the case, followed by a double note if the first quarter had passed, two double notes for the half-hour and three for the third quarter. The system is called 'quarter repeating'.

In the eighteenth century, many repeating watches using Quare's invention were made in Geneva. The button or push-piece to make the repeater work was in the knob of the pendant on the case. Pressing it wound a spring, and releasing it caused the spring to operate the repeating mechanism which struck on a bell.

Some repeating watches, particularly by French makers, had a projecting pin known as a 'pulse piece' near the bottom of the case. If pressed while the watch was repeating, the blows of the hammer were received by the finger, so the repeater could be used by deaf people.

In the last quarter of the eighteenth century, Breguet, and also Le Roy, working in France, replaced the bell by steel rods which acted as gongs and took up much less space. Before this Le Roy had attempted to reduce case thickness by eliminating the bell and causing the hammer to strike a block on the case. Several makers produced these watches, called 'dumb repeaters'.

In the last part of the nineteenth century, the operating button was moved to the side of the case because the position in the pendant was required for the keyless winding button. The push piece became a slide which was moved a short distance round the edge of the case and released.

English watchmakers of the eighteenth century occasionally produced a half-quarter repeater watch. After sounding the last hour by single strokes on a bell, the quarters were given by double strokes and then another blow on the bell was given if the time was more than $7\frac{1}{2}$ minutes past the quarter. Minute repeaters were made by Arnold, Breguet, and others, from the end of the eighteenth century onwards, but in the later nineteenth, except for a few isolated examples, and were mainly a preserve of the Swiss. Two or three gongs of different pitch were fitted, the hour being struck on the low one, the quarters by a blow on each and the minutes by blows on the higher. Thus: tang, tang, tang . . . ting-tang, ting-tang . . . ting, ting, ting, ting, ting, ting, ting . . . was seven minutes after half past three.

The Swiss combined repeater mechanisms with automata in many of their elaborate watches and before the second half of the nineteenth century had built up a big export business in them. The use of gongs considerable reduced the size of the case.

Musical watches were also made in comfortable numbers in Geneva in the nineteenth century. The earliest had a disc with pins each side to pluck a musical comb. Soon a barrel was adopted for cheaper models, as employed in musical alarms and boxes. Sometimes musical movements were fitted into seals, for carrying on watch chains, and also into snuff boxes.

Most popular automata on watch dials were those showing little figures striking a gong at the hour, or when the repeater was operated. The true gongs were inside the movement, of course. Other favourites were Father Time striking with his scythe, animated pastoral scenes, a revolving mill wheel with an angler nearby, a knife-grinder, a woman at a spinning wheel, two cupids at a blacksmith's, and various musicians. See-saws, like that shown in Plate 96 were also common. Rotating glass rods imitate running water in the watch in Plate 87.

Singing birds were produced in large numbers at this time by the Swiss makers, but rarely fitted into watch mechanisms. Most were set in snuff-boxes.

The Swiss also specialized in secret pornographic watches in the later nineteenth century. Pressing a secret spring caused a suggestive picture to appear. Most of the pictures were animated. Some were in the collection of King Farouk of Egypt catalogued by Sotheby's in London some years ago, and one that passed through the sale without its mechanism being spotted caused considerable embarrassment to the clergyman who was showing it to a lady who inadvertently touched the secret spring.

Moon dials, sidereal dials, perpetual calendars, up and down dials, times of sunset and sunrise, and planetaria, appeared on watches. The mechanisms were as described in Chapter 13. An equation watch with an extra minute hand recording solar time is shown in Plate 97; round the outer edge is an annual calendar. The extremely complicated watch in Plate 98 was made by Leroy of Paris in 1897 to special order for 20,000 francs. Among the complications are a perpetual calendar giving the day, date, month and year for 100 years; phases and age of the moon; seasons; solstices, equinoxes; and equation of time. There is a chronograph with zero fly-back, and minute and hour counters, and an up-and-down dial. The watch will strike grande sonnerie, or petite sonnerie, or be silent; and the hours, quarters, and minutes can be repeated on three notes. Astronomical dials for Paris and Lisbon are operated by a sidereal gear train. Local time is given for 125 of the world's towns, and also the time of rising and setting of the sun in Lisbon. Incorporated in the watch are a thermometer, a barometer, and a hygrometer. On top of that, it can be regulated without opening it – just as well, maybe!

Another double-dialled complicated watch is that in Plate 99; only the front dial is illustrated. It was made by Abraham-Louis Breguet and sold by him in 1807 for 5,160 francs to General Junot, one of Napoleon's most illustrious generals. Eventually it came into possession of the Duke of Wellington and was sold at Sotheby's in London by his heir for a record price for a watch of £27,500 in 1965. The front engine-turned dial is of gold and the back one of platinum. On the rear dial is a year calendar and age and phases of the moon. A still later complicated watch can be seen in Plate 100. It was made about 1910–20 and was sold as a regular line at £500 by S. Smith and Sons of Strand, London, the small jewellers that became Smiths Industries. The movement was English and the complicated work Swiss, except for the two parts – the chronograph work and the tourbillon carriage (see page 173) which were by Nicole Neilsen of Soho, London. The dial shows time of day, day of the week, day of the month and month, the calendar being perpetual, i.e. compensating for leap years. There is a moon dial and age of moon hand. The chronograph, or stop-watch action, is performed by two push buttons on the side of the case, and gives split seconds, i.e. there are two centre seconds hands, one above the other, one of which can be stopped to obtain a reading, then made to catch up the other. Minutes elapsed when the chronograph is in action are read on a minute recording hand which is over the year calendar hand. In the illustration, these and the split seconds hands are on top of each other.

A chronograph is, strictly speaking, any form of instrument for measuring short intervals of time, whether of clock, watch or other form. The earliest method, employed in the eighteenth century, was to employ an ordinary watch and stop and restart the whole gear train by a lever which pressed on one of the moving parts. This was the primitive stop watch.

In 1776, a Swiss maker, Pouzait, invented a watch with a centre seconds hand that jumped from second to second and could be stopped without stopping the watch itself, in other words, a watch with an independent dead seconds hand. It was actually the first chronograph. The next step was the invention of the seconds hand that would return to zero when required and restart from there. It was invented by Nicole and Capt, of Switzerland, and first shown at the London Exhibition of 1862. The split seconds chronograph was invented soon after this.

PRECIOUS METAL CASES

First quality watches in gold cases and second quality ones in silver can usually be dated much more accurately than clocks because those made in England had to be assayed for quality and hallmarked by the Worshipful Company of Goldsmiths. Gold cases were generally marked from about 1685, although it was not the rule with silver cases until the 1740s. By identifying the date letter of the hallmark, it is possible to date the case within a year, but hallmarks were extensively forged, especially those of 1790 to 1830.

Earlier silver cases from about 1680 are found with initials stamped in them, but these are the casemaker's and give no indication of date. At this time casemakers were members of the Clockmakers Company and only subject to the Goldsmiths Company for the quality of precious metals they used.

A hallmark normally consists of four stamps: the maker's mark, the quality mark, the date letter, and the hallmark itself which shows where the case was assayed. As date letters ran in different phases in different assay offices and were repeated in different styles, it is impossible to remember them, but there are low-priced booklets on the market such as 'Hallmarks and Date Letters' (N.A.G. Press Ltd) which list them over about five centuries.

To save the cost of gold, which was usually of 22 carat quality, i.e. 22 parts fine gold in 24, some cases were made in silver gilt, which has the same appearance, although the hallmark is for silver. The case is made of silver then covered by a film of gold by the mercuric gilding process, also called 'fire gilding'. An amalgam paste of mercury and powdered gold is rubbed on the silver and the case heated, which vaporizes the mercury and causes the gold to amalgamate with the silver. The process is not now used as it is dangerous to health. It produced a thicker coating than most electro-plate.

An imitation gold was invented by a watch and clockmaker, Christopher Pinchbeck (1657–1713). It is actually four parts copper to three zinc. Pinchbeck, as the metal itself was named, was used for watch cases. An alloy of aluminium and bronze was also employed after 1862.

ENAMELLING

Enamel is actually glass melted on to a metal surface – on to gold or copper (and rarely brass) for watch cases, although bronze and iron were also enamelled for other purposes. Even a hard glass was enamelled in Arab mosque lamps of the thirteenth century.

The earliest form of decorative enamelling for cases was called champlevé. The pattern is made on the metal case or dial by carving or hollowing the surface into a series of cells. In each compartment is placed frit of the appropriate colour and the whole fired in a furnace until the frit melts and becomes a coloured glass in each compartment. Sometimes the surface of the metal was formed into a pattern of cells by strips of metal, which were filled with enamel. This is called cloisonné enamelling. Both methods were used for early watches. Champlevé was employed for both cases and dials; cloisonné was never used for dials.

Both cloisonné and champlevé enamelling can be distinguished by the metal lines between the areas of colour. Extra patterns were made near the end of the nineteenth century by pieces of gold foil placed on the enamel and a flux over that, called 'paillonné'.

Enamelled decoration on watches was first employed about the beginning of the seventeenth century. Some hundred years earlier, in Limoges in France, a method of decoration by painting with different coloured enamels had been discovered by mixing them with gum instead of firing them in cells in the metal. It was applied to plaques, reliquaries and such objects, but only rarely to watch cases. About 1630, however, a French goldsmith, Jean Toutin, invented a method of painting oxides on to a ground of white enamel, which was very suitable for watch cases, as delicate results could be achieved.

During the first half of the seventeenth century, magnificent painted enamel watch cases were turned out by Blois enamellers, most of them depicting flowers, but others with scenes or portraits. Such watches are now both rare and very valuable.

Enamelling was also carried out in Paris, London, and Geneva. It was in Geneva, however, that it flourished and has continued as one of the town's most famous crafts until the present day. The most celebrated Genevan enamellers were the family of Huaud, active in the second half of the seventeenth century. Many of their pictures included buxom women partly unclothed.

Incidentally, cases of gold and copper were paper thin and were always enamelled inside as well as outside to avoid the case buckling. Even late Geneva separate cases were contra-enamelled.

About 1600 a form of enamelling known as 'basse-taille' was introduced mainly for dials. The ground was engraved in a pattern of foliage, birds' feathers, etc., and a thin layer of transparent coloured enamel fired over it. About 1670 enamelling was employed over a regular pattern of hand engraving and called 'flinqué'. When engine-turning was introduced, enamelling was applied over this, a decoration called 'guilloché', which came in about 1800.

Enamelling as a craft developed to such an extent in Geneva during the eighteenth century that, at the turn into the nineteenth, its enamelled watches, musical boxes, and other novelties were being exported all over the world. Designs included portraits, flowers, scenes of many kinds, and mythological subjects.

Plain white dials with black figures and indications were enamelled in the same way as decorative cases and dials. Incidentally, fine hair cracks are sometimes seen in old white enamel dials, also chipped areas, especially around winding holes. There is no known way of repairing these satisfactorily – or if there is, it is a well-guarded secret.

16 Technical Changes in Watches

MOST German watches were entirely of iron, up to about 1600. A few were made in brass. Makers attempted to improve the time-keeping, which was very inferior to clocks of the period, by using the stackfreed described in Chapter 10. A few, particularly in Augsburg, employed the fusee. The French industry was more progressive, introducing brass for the plates and very soon for the wheels too, meshing them with steel pinions, a practice which is universal today. The French also favoured the much more satisfactory fusee instead of the stackfreed to provide a more even output from the mainspring.

French watches had wheel balances, whereas bar balances are often found on German watches. Teeth were particularly well cut on the French brass wheels. The plates of all early watches were held together by pillars riveted to one plate and fastened to the other one by taper pins, as with early clocks. From about 1620, however, watches incorporated a single screw, to fasten the balance cock to the back plate.

All early watches with fusees had catgut line from the barrel to the fusee, but after about 1670, small chains like miniature bicycle chains were introduced. The fusees for these were cut with square-sectioned instead of round-sectioned grooves. Chain drive was employed some forty years earlier on clocks and it was presumably not possible or economic to make them small enough then for watches (Fig. 13).

The escapement was the verge and crown wheel and the time controller a balance without a balance spring. It was driven by a train of three or four wheels to give a going time of half a day, so watches had to be wound twice daily. In the second half of the seventeenth century makers began to incorporate a fourth wheel in the train of gears to provide a going time of about twenty-six hours and reduce winding to once daily.

158

Regulation of the fusee watch was crude, by using a key to turn the squared end of the spring barrel, which projected through the back plate and was provided with a ratchet and click. This altered the 'set-up' or amount of power exerted by the spring. Regulation of the stackfreed was even cruder, by setting up the stopwork and adjusting the hog's bristles, described in Chapter 10.

As the watch was a bad timekeeper until the last quarter of the seventeenth century, undue attention was probably paid to decoration and novelty. Introduction of the spiral balance spring revolutionized timekeeping. It is not known for certain to whom credit should be given for its invention, but it was either the Englishman Dr Robert Hooke, or the Dutchman Christiaan Huygens. Both claimed it. It was introduced soon after 1675.

The balance spring for watches represented a similar leap forward in accuracy as the pendulum for clocks, although not immediately so far. In effect the two inventions were very similar. The pendulum employed the constant force of gravity as a 'spring' to keep it oscillating accurately. The balance was provided with a spiral spring which tried to hold it in its central or rest position, like the force of gravity operating on the pendulum.

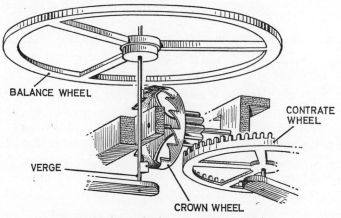

FIG. 26. Right-angle drive in a verge watch.

Benefits of the balance and spring combination encouraged watchmakers to attempt other improvements which help now to date a watch. Nevertheless, the verge escapement driven from a contrate wheel, as shown in Fig. 26, one of the very earliest arrangements, continued to be employed for nearly four hundred years despite the awkwardness of the right-angled drive.

CYLINDER ESCAPEMENT

The combination of fusee with verge escapement made the watch rather fat. It involved a right-angle drive to the escapement. Early in the eighteenth century technically advanced watchmakers in London began to experiment with what has become known as the 'cylinder' escapement, also called the 'horizontal' escapement. This was at first fitted to the same basic movements as the fusee.

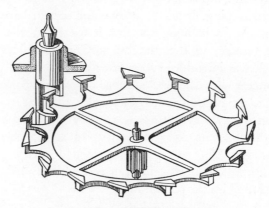

FIG. 27. The cylinder escapement.

It has an escape wheel with hook-like teeth on pins and can easily be recognized. As shown in Fig. 27, the teeth act directly on a cylinder which is part of the staff or axle of the balance wheel. It was first used commercially by George Graham and Thomas Tompion in London on some special watches. In 1728, George Graham sent an example to Julien LeRoy, an eminent French maker, and LeRoy liked it so much that he adopted it. The final result was that it became more popular in France and Switzerland than in other watchmaking countries.

Until about 1750 almost every watch had a verge escapement or a cylinder escapement, the latter being most favoured for high grade movements. The verge continued in use until as late as about 1880 for popular watches and the cylinder into the present century. Unfortunately, the cylinder escapement had a brass escape wheel and steel cylinder which were subject to rapid wear, and from about 1770 the few top makers in several countries began using steel escape wheels with cylinders cut from ruby. Most successful of these was A. L. Breguet.

After the middle of the eighteenth century, different types of escapements began to appear, mainly from English makers, who retained their lead in invention and precision timekeeping, although they had lost the battle of fashions to France.

ORMSKIRK ESCAPEMENT

One of these was the invention of Peter Debaufré early in the century and was taken up enthusiastically by makers in Lancashire, who were competing with London. It is sometimes known as the 'Ormskirk' escapement, because it was made in large numbers in that town around 1800, and also the 'clubfoot', and the 'chaffcutter', because it has a double escape wheel reminiscent of the two scything blades of a chaff cutter. It was also employed on clocks, in a form with club-shaped teeth to the escape wheel, invented in 1830 by Paris maker, Paul Garnier.

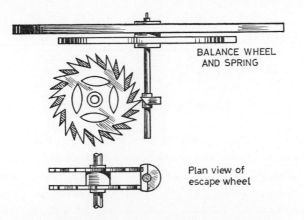

BALANCE WHEEL
AND SPRING

Plan view of
escape wheel

FIG. 28. The chaff-cutter or Ormskirk escapement.

From the illustration, Fig. 28, it will be seen that the escape wheel acts directly on the balance staff, like the cylinder, but it is not horizontal and had to have the same contrate (right-angled) drive as a verge, but it was cheap to make, unlike the cylinder, and gave much the same performance, although with the same rapid rate of wear. It is found on watches up to the first quarter of the nineteenth century.

RACK LEVER

Another successful escapement was invented in 1722 and was also taken up in Lancashire, particularly by Peter Litherland of Liverpool but not until almost the end of the century. It, too, was made in large numbers and is called the 'rack lever'. One is shown in Fig. 29.

FIG. 29. The rack lever escapement.

What had been lacking in a watch after the invention of the balance spring was the equivalent of the anchor escapement which had been so successful in clocks. The rack lever was a form of Graham dead beat escapement. The swinging balance was linked to the anchor escapement not by a crutch, however, but by a toothed rack acting on a toothed pinion on the staff of the balance wheel. This arrangement allowed the balance to swing through nearly two complete turns instead of the limited arc of other escapements.

VIRGULE ESCAPEMENT

French watches made over a period of about twenty years at the end of the eighteenth century sometimes had an escapement called the virgule, which can be recognized by a piece like a comma on the staff of the balance and the vertical pins on the tips of the teeth of the escape wheel. It was most used by Lepine, and is in action an improved version of the cylinder escapement, although it was more difficult to make.

DUPLEX ESCAPEMENT

For the highest grade watches, still another escapement was preferred. Reversing what had become the more usual trend, it was invented in France in its practical form by Pierre LeRoy, and was taken up by English makers more than any others, from the last decade of the eighteenth century through almost three-quarters of the nineteenth. The escapement is known as the 'duplex', because it has two sets of

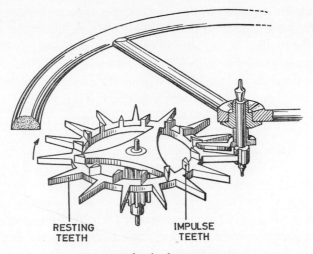

RESTING
TEETH

IMPULSE
TEETH

FIG. 30. The duplex escapement.

teeth on the escape wheel separating the functions of impulsing the balance wheel by the escape wheel and unlocking the escape wheel by the balance. These double teeth can be seen in a duplex watch. One set are pointed, long, and radial; the other set are small wedges on the rim of the escape wheel. The balance staff has a long, pointed pallet, like the comma of the virgule, but straight (Fig. 30). On rare occasions a duplex watch is found with two escape wheels, one for each set of teeth.

One version of the duplex was made particularly in the town of Fleurier, in Switzerland, from about 1850, and is called the 'Chinese duplex' because it was intended for that market. Such a watch is easily recognizable for several reasons. The cases were brightly enamelled and the movement was particularly elaborately embellished with not only intricate engraving but many little curves to the edges of the bridges on the back plate. The chief characteristic was a dead beat sweep seconds hand, which is quite sophisticated in a watch even today. The seconds hand was centred with the other hands. The escape wheel teeth were released every half-second, but each tooth had a small notch in the end of it, so that as the seconds hand turned, it made one tiny jump that could hardly be seen, then a large one. The hand appeared, therefore, to jump every second.

CHRONOMETER ESCAPEMENT

The search for precision in England, enormously encouraged by an Act of Parliament offering the then staggering sum of £20,000 for 'solving the longitude', resulted in the development of the detent or chronometer escapement by Thos. Earnshaw and John Arnold. Although the principal use was in marine chronometers, as explained in another chapter, the detent escapement (Fig. 31) was also incorporated in many high grade watches, usually called 'pocket chronometers', which were first made in quantity by Arnold and by Earnshaw in the last quarter of the eighteenth century and continued to be made and much sought after as precision watches through the nineteenth and into the twentieth.

The escapement of the pocket chronometer should not be confused with that of today's 'wrist chronometer', which has a lever escapement, the Swiss having annexed the word 'chronometer' because of

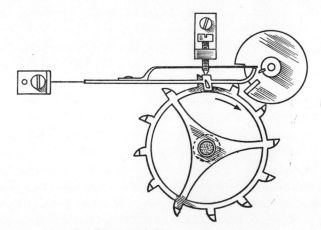

FIG. 31. The Arnold chronometer escapement.

its high performance connotation for their watches which have reached certain performance standards. Swiss makers used to make true pocket chronometers, however.

Although it improved the accuracy of a watch considerably, the detent escapement is more affected than others by sudden movement of the watch and is also not self-starting. It has an escape wheel with short, stubby, pointed teeth at an acute angle. These impulse the balance directly by acting on a ruby pallet on the balance staff. Locking and unlocking of the escape wheel is carried out by a separate lever – the detent. The word 'detent' (from a root word meaning 'to unhold or release') is used for any lever that holds up a spring or locks something.

In this case, the balance wheel, as it swings, moves aside a detent which is holding up a tooth of the escape wheel. The tooth jumps forward and impulses the balance before the next tooth is stopped by the detent. On the return swing of the balance, what is called a 'passing spring' prevents the escape wheel from being unlocked.

The chronometer or detent escapement therefore allows the hands to jump at every other swing of the balance instead of every swing, like most other escapements. Some chronometers were designed to give dead half-seconds.

Larger versions of pocket chronometers were made for use on board ship to carry the time from the place where a sun or star observation was made to the ship's marine chronometer, which would never be moved except in emergency. Such watches are still employed today and are called 'deck watches'. They look like large pocket watches and are kept in special boxes like marine chronometers, but now have lever escapements.

DETACHED LEVER ESCAPEMENT

The lever escapement, which eventually ousted the others was invented in 1770 by Thomas Mudge, an Englishman, but not developed by him. The balance and hairspring were allowed to oscillate freely by being detached from – not directly connected to – the rest of the watch movement. The only connection was when the swinging balance unlocked and relocked the train of gears from the mainspring and, between these two actions, was given an impulse to keep it swinging. This whole sequence took on by a fraction of a second.

The detached lever escapement, as it should strictly be called, was

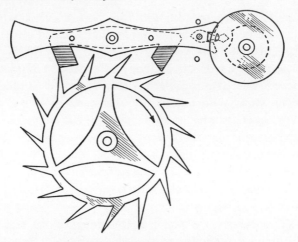

FIG. 32. The English lever escapement.

experimented with and developed by various makers, including Emery, Massey, Pendleton, and Leroux, but detached lever watches were not made in any quantity until English makers took it up enthusiastically in the nineteenth century after a separate line of development from Peter Litherland's rack lever mentioned earlier. The English lever had a pointed toothed escape wheel and a lever like the anchor escapement of a clock (Fig. 32). Lever escapements are called 'anchor' on the continent.

The balance spring itself had received the attention of makers who were concerned with precision. The early springs of around 1750 had only a few turns because of the difficulty of making them. They were of untempered steel and were therefore soft. The technique of making improved to such an extent that four and even five turns became usual, and gave the best performance with a verge escapement. Before the third quarter of the eighteenth century had run out, makers were using steel spring which had been hardened and tempered to blue. When the lever escapement came into use after 1800, the length of the balance spring was increased to provide about ten turns because of the bigger arc of swing of the balance wheel. Today that number is sometimes doubled.

Arnold and other chronometer makers began to use helical balance springs (like a spiral staircase) instead of flat spiral ones for their pocket chronometers in an attempt to reduce timekeeping errors. The ends were curved inwards to avoid wobbling of the spring as it was twisted by the balance wheel.

When a flat spring winds and unwinds with the balance wheel, it expands and contracts (i.e. 'breathes') unevenly because it is attached to a fixed point at its outer end, which affects timekeeping. Later in the century, Breguet found that if the outer coil of a flat spring were given an upwards kink and curved inwards it could be made almost as isochronous as a cylindrical spring, so the 'Breguet overcoil' came into use for most precision watches.

REGULATION

Before the introduction of the balance spring, when adjustments were made to the tension of the mainspring (the set-up) to adjust timekeeping, a regulator was employed to make the task easier. It comprised a gear wheel on the mainspring arbor which could be turned by a worm wheel. A numbered disc on the gearwheel indicated which way it should be turned to increase or decrease the rate. One is shown in Plate 101. The worm wheel (the bar at top left) was turned by a key which fitted over one end.

When the balance spring came into use, it provided another means of regulation, by shortening or lengthening its effective length. A watchmaker, Nathaniel Barrow, invented a straight threaded rod with a nut on it. Turning the threaded rod by means of a key moved a two-pin 'clamp' on the nut along the fixed end of the balance spring. Barrow regulators were used on some early English balance and spring watches. Their disadvantage was that the regulator moved in a straight line.

The next step, devised by Thomas Tompion, was to provide a gearwheel with a numbered disc (like that for the mainspring) which turned a toothed sector and moved the clamp in an arc round the outer coil of the balance spring. It was employed by many makers, in England and on the continent, sometimes with a means of altering mainspring set-up as well with fusee watches. See Plates 101 and 102. The key was applied to a square on the centre of the wheel of Tompion's regulator, which was employed on most eighteenth-century watches.

An even simpler system, which first appeared at the beginning of the eighteenth century, was to have a lever which turned about the same centre as the balance wheel and carried two pins (curb pins) to restrict the active length of the hairspring. It was mounted on the plate under the balance spring (Plate 103). Towards the end of the century, the same system was employed, but *over* the balance spring, the index lever being on the watch cock (Plate 104). It soon superseded all earlier types.

Regulators were also employed with an overcoil. Many precision watches were very accurately adjusted, and the final adjustments made by small screws around the rim of the balance wheel. Such watches are called 'free-sprung'. Free-sprung pocket watches were made throughout the nineteenth century and are still made today for very accurate wrist as well as pocket watches.

TEMPERATURE COMPENSATION

A trouble of makers of precision watches was caused by temperature changes expanding or contracting the metal of the spring and the balance and upsetting timekeeping. It was partly solved by making the balance wheel rim of two metals, one of which expanded more than the other, and cutting the rim in two places, so that each 'spoke' carried a scythe-shaped section of rim. As temperature increased, the free ends of the bi-metallic rim bent inwards to compensate for the increasing length of the 'spokes' and varying elasticity of the balance spring.

Precision timekeeping was revolutionized in 1899 by the invention by Frenchman, Dr C.-E. Guillaume, of an alloy called 'Invar' that did not vary in size at different temperatures. It was first used for balances and later another alloy was invented by him for balance springs. The invention of Invar won him a Nobel Prize.

Even before 1700 makers began to think that a balance wheel of large diameter gave better timekeeping than a small one. Balance wheels were made of steel with three spokes, usually, until fairly late in the eighteenth century when brass came into increasing favour with two spokes, called a 'crossing'.

In the eighteenth century, English makers concentrated on higher precision and their watches became about a quarter of an inch thicker – about $1\frac{1}{4}$ inches – because of the balance and spring on the back plate. French watches were thicker still, at $1\frac{1}{2}$ inches, and became known as 'oignons' (onions). The Swiss also followed the French in this. Towards the end of the eighteenth century, however, the position had reversed, with the French making thinner watches than the English. The English watches were more reliable; the French were, perhaps, more accurate, but lost their 'tune' earlier.

MOVEMENT DESIGN

The quest for thinness had (and indeed still has) a very strong in-fluence on technical design. At first, watch movements comprised two plates held together by pillars, with the balance outside the back plate under a balance cock. (A bridge is a part that looks like a bridge and is fixed at both ends by screws. Its purpose is to provide a pivot bearing. A cock is like half a bridge, held only at one end, and also used to carry a bearing, i.e. there is a hole in it for a pivot to turn. The balance cock takes one pivot of the balance.) The pillar and plate arrangement is called a 'full plate movement'. In the eighteenth century some makers began to use a back plate that did not cover the whole area, only about three-quarters or half of it. The object was to sink the balance and its cock within the width of the plates. The system continued through the nineteenth and into this century (Plate 109). Makers like J. F. Cole and McCabe also experimented in the nineteenth century with movements in which most wheels were under separate cocks and could be removed independently.

But it was earlier, in 1770, that the French maker, Antoine Lepine, introduced a system of construction that gradually changed all watch-making. Instead of a back plate, he used a series of cocks or bridges to hold the pivots of the train wheels as well as the balance, which brought them into the same plane as the other wheels. Such move-ments are also called 'bar' or 'barred' movements.

French makers took rapidly to the Lepine calibre (Plate 106) and also began using a going barrel instead of the much thicker fusee. The English persisted with their full plates and fusees. From just before 1800, therefore, and throughout the nineteenth century, the French watch was thin and the English one fat, but more reliable.

WINDING

Before 1800 watches were wound by a key, usually from the back. French oignons and a few others, including Breguet's 'souscription' watches (with one hand, the only ones he made alike, and to a price), had a winding square through the boss of the hand. Keys were often elaborately pierced and carved and sometimes set with moss agate and other gem materials (Plate 106).

About 1800, makers became interested in keyless winding. The earliest version that came into use was 'pump-winding'. A plunger (which also carried the bow or loop for attaching the watch to a chain) was pushed in and out a few times to wind the mainspring.

The method of winding a watch by turning the pendant knob was patented by an Englishman, T. Prest, who was Arnold's foreman, in 1820. It was not popular with English makers because it could not be applied to fusee watches, only going barrel ones. The first watch in which the button was used for setting the hands and for winding, as it is today, was invented by Adrien Philippe in 1842, and a few years later made by the firm of Patek, Philippe and Co., but took a long time to be readily accepted (Plate 107).

Some ingenious keyless winding systems were applied to fusee watches, but only high grade ones; the others were still key wound. Most English watches with going barrels had what is called a 'rocking bar' keyless mechanism in the later nineteenth and early twentieth centuries. By the side of the winding button was a small projecting piece which had to be pressed with a fingernail, so that turning the button would set the hands instead of winding the mainspring.

JEWELS

The use of jewels in watches, to provide freer and better wear-resisting bearings for the wheel pivots, was employed at an early period. It was invented in 1704 by a Swiss and two French watch-makers working in England. English watchmakers began to employ jewels from about 1715 and kept the method of manufacture a secret for about a hundred years from their competitors on the continent. A late version known as Liverpool jewelling is shown in Plate 108. Pierced natural rubies were the first 'jewels', with other natural gemstones, including garnet which was really too soft. Diamond was commonly introduced as an 'endstone' in the balance cock after the first quarter of the eighteenth century, to take the end thrust of the balance wheel pivot. One is seen in Plate 103. Today synthetic ruby is used.

OILING

Providing a watch with oil that will last and stay in place for a long period was always a problem and still is. Breguet is supposed to have answered Napoleon's request for a perfect watch with the remark, 'Give me a perfect oil, and I will give you a perfect watch.' From about 1750 watchmakers began using a simple system of oil retention that had been invented some thirty-five years earlier. Small cups, called 'oil sinks', were made around pivots on the outsides of plates.

BREGUET

A. L. Breguet (1747–1823), who worked in Paris, except during the Revolution when he returned to his home in Switzerland, was responsible for many original contributions to watchmaking. His watches were of such perfection of finish, such ingenuity, and in some cases of such complexity, that no one before or since has been able to match him. They have a modern appearance much ahead of other makers of his time. Most of his movements were half plates, but many were 'barred' (with bridges instead of a back plate, i.e. Lepine calibre). He modified the cylinder escapement to improve it, employing a ruby cylinder on an extension below the balance pivot. He was one of the first to use the detached lever escapement, and also introduced shock-absorbing for the balance pivot, which he called a 'parachute'. The balance jewels were mounted on the ends of strips of springy steel which gave under shock.

The self-winding pocket watch, invented by Perrelet in Switzerland, was perfected by Breguet, and patented by Recordon in London. Breguet made a number with lever escapements between 1780 and 1800. Self-winding movements are shown in Plates 88 and 89. A weighted lever across the back bounces with movements of the wearer and winds the mainspring. Another version, not by Breguet, had a rotor instead of an oscillating weight.

In common with other makers, Breguet sometimes made watches which could be used in the dark, and by blind people, called 'montres á tact' in France. One by LeRoy is shown in Plate 110. A raised arrow on the case is turned until it stops and the time found by touch in relation to the turquoise projections marking the hours round the edge of the case. The key shown in this plate is a special type known as a 'tipsy key', which has a ratchet so that it will wind only in one direction.

ENGLISH LEVER

English makers continued in their quest for increasing accuracy and were supreme in chronometry, making most of the world's marine chronometers during the nineteenth century. At the same time they had developed the lever escapement which, with a fusee, gave a fine performance in ordinary watches. The 'English' lever became internationally famous: at this period it was the Rolls-Royce of the watch industries.

The English lever had an escape wheel with pointed teeth. To avoid wear on the tips of pointed escape wheel teeth and give certain technical advantages, Breguet invented a stubby shape known as a 'club tooth', which became gradually universal and was particularly applicable to watches made by machine.

MACHINE MAKING

During the nineteenth century there were many attempts to mechanize watchmaking, particularly by Japy in France at the beginning of the century, and by Dennison in North America later. The most persistent were the Swiss, who finally succeeded in setting up a largely mechanized industry. The English had 80,000 craft workers in Clerkenwell, London, in Coventry, in Prescot, and in other centres in 1800. They refused to accept attempts at mechanization and in the first quarter of the next century English watchmaking had dwindled almost to nothing.

One of the finest English makers of the nineteenth century was James Ferguson Cole, called 'the English Breguet' because he corresponded with Breguet and some of his work was very similar. Others were Robt. Roskell, John R. Arnold, son of the original chronometer maker, E. J. Dent and his son Frederick, Charles Frodsham, Jurgensen, Pendleton, Barraud and Sons, later Barraud and Lund, and Bonniksen.

After the turn of the twentieth century, only a few makers were left in England, principally Rotherham and Sons of Coventry, who were producing pocket watches from 1750 to 1940, when their factory was bombed and burnt out. A number of firms bought raw watch movements (the unfinished bits and pieces) and carried out the last and most critical stages of manufacture. These included Nicole Nielsen of Soho Square, who went out of business in 1935, and Usher and Cole, H. Golay, and Charles Frodsham, all of which are still in existence.

TOURBILLON AND KARRUSEL

Owing to the effects of gravity on balance, hairspring, and escapement, and to varying friction on bearings according to whether they are horizontal or vertical, a watch has never been made that will go at the same rate in different positions. The extreme skill of the watch adjuster lies in his ability to reduce and average out these errors. In general a watch will gain on its back or dial, and lose when on edge, but this is an extreme simplification. Breguet invented a device called a 'tourbillon' which virtually eliminated positional errors of a pocket watch kept in a pocket. The lever escapement was in a cage which itself rotated every minute so that all the errors in different vertical positions averaged out.

Bahn Bonniksen of Coventry invented in 1894 a simplified version of the system which he called the 'karrusel', after the Swedish name for 'roundabout'. One is shown in Plate 109. Many were made by Bonniksen and other makers. The carriage holding the escapement rotates in a slower period, once in $52\frac{1}{2}$ minutes. In 1903 Bonniksen patented what he called 'Bonniksen's tourbillon watch', in which the carriage rotated in 39 minutes.

While an ordinary collector is never likely to come across a Breguet tourbillon, he may find one by a later maker – many were made in Neuchâtel in Switzerland over the turn of the nineteenth century – or perhaps a karrusel watch. Rotherham and Sons still had a karrusel for sale in 1959 – the last they had made and had not bothered to show anyone. A highly ingenious version of the rotating principle of eliminating timekeeping errors was employed in the Waterbury watch, described on page 146.

Anyone intending to start watch collecting on a limited budget could probably find it ultimately profitable and would certainly find it interesting to concentrate on the transitional period when experiments were being carried out in machine manufacture.

17 How to Buy a Timepiece

EVERYONE likes a bargain, collector or dealer, and the real bargains arise through having more knowledge than the next man. A collector with sound knowledge gains experience and builds a collection of merit and value. A dealer with knowledge of horology tends to specialize and to buy only what he believes himself to be genuine. Even the best make mistakes on occasions, because no one ever knew all there is to know about the subject, and it is possible to be 100 per cent right on authenticity and make a mistake over the price – or completely misjudge the cost of restoration or repair. Nevertheless, the specialist dealer is much less likely to make mistakes and much more likely to cover what mistakes he does make by not passing them on to customers. His reputation as a specialist would be at stake.

This leads to the proposition that someone unsure of himself intending to start a collection would be wise to go to a horological dealer. He should get what he pays for and the piece should have been cleaned and put in going order if that is possible. A furniture dealer who sells clocks is very rarely interested in what is inside them, although this may make a big difference to the true value. He will sell one 'in going order', but that does not mean the movement has been serviced or even looked at; only that he wound it and it ticked. There are a few exceptions, of course. When sure of himself, it is in this area that the collector may be able to find a bargain.

Conversions are a problem. There are many clocks that had verge and foliot control or verge and balance and were converted to pendulum, or were converted from verge to anchor escapement, and many watches converted from some other escapement to lever. Today large numbers of French carriage clocks are being converted from cylinder escapement to lever. At all times, owners have wanted their clocks to be serviceable. It is only when the clocks gain value because of their age and authenticity that the owners begin to wonder whether the clocks should be restored. Specialist dealers, naturally, have expert work done on cases and movements to bring them back as near as possible to pristine state, but there are arguments about how much is permissible, and it is generally accepted that some conversions made in the past are acceptable.

Apart from restoration, at all times in their history, most old clocks and watches had worn or damaged parts replaced at some time or another. Many may have had entirely 'new' movements or cases. These can hardly be called 'wrong' if it was the practice at an earlier time to replace movements.

These factors affect the value of a timepiece as do a number of others. What is the value of an antique clock or watch? The question is often asked. A few dealers will give an instant price. Others are so guarded that any monetary value they might be persuaded to suggest they hedge at once with 'ifs' and 'buts'. There is a short answer; the value is the highest price you can expect to get from a buyer. It depends entirely on the buyer. If there is no potential buyer, it is ludicrous to talk about a monetary value. That is one reason why valuations vary. Take an American clock. One valuer may put £10 on it because he knows it will fetch a low price in the UK. A second valuer may price it at £40 because he happens to have regular American customers. Which is the true value? It depends upon the market and that may well depend upon the time when the clock might be offered for sale.

Briefly, these are major factors affecting price:

1. Generally, the older the more valuable, but not always. A seventeenth-century longcase clock will normally fetch more than an earlier lantern clock.

2. The more original and the better the condition, the higher the price.

3. The more complex, the higher the price, but not always. The value as a piece of furniture may outweigh the technical value.

4. The higher the original quality, the higher the price today.

5. The maker's name. Identical clocks with different makers' names on them fetch widely differing prices. These were 'bread and butter' lines supplied to various 'makers'.

6. Longer going time always attracts more value.

7. Practicality. In general old clocks are more practical than old watches as they will still perform as timekeepers, some very well. An antique clock is usually more than just an item of furniture. Watches

are more purely collectors' items, except perhaps for some of the later ones.

8. Artistic merit. Ugly timepieces do not attract the best prices.

9. Fashion. This is a big factor. For example, fine grandfather clocks nine feet tall are not easy to sell because few people have rooms big enough for them. The same is true of large table clocks. This keeps down the price. Again, an oak case will depress a price when oak is out of favour for furnishing.

SETTING-UP A CLOCK

Having bought a clock, the first problem is to get it home undamaged. A horological dealer will advise on this point, or deliver and set it up for his customer. If the clock is bought from an uninformed source, the new owner must know what he is about.

Make sure that it is complete as far as it is possible to judge, including keys, weights, and any ornaments not firmly attached. Spring-driven clocks are easiest to manage. If pendulum controlled, open the back of the case to see if there is a hook to which the pendulum can be fastened for transit. In earlier bracket or table clocks the short pendulum rod should be flexed slightly to push it under a hook provided on the back plate. On later ones, there is often a thumb screw with a plate to hold the pendulum in a fixed position. If there is no anchorage, the pendulum will have spring or silk suspension, and can be removed by raising it slightly to bring the top of the spring forward out of its slot, or to unhook the pendulum rod from the silk loop. It will then be necessary to move the pendulum downwards through the hole in the crutch to remove it. Some types of crutch have a slot or pin instead of a hole which makes the task easier.

The movement will now run down at a faster rate, but come to no harm. To stop it, particularly if it is a chime or strike, place a thickly folded strip of tissue paper as a wedge between the plate and the crutch.

Never, in any circumstances, dismantle a spring-driven clock when the springs are wound up. They must be completely run down, and even then great care is necessary. A wound clock when dismantled can explode and cause very serious injury.

When you get the clock home, re-attach the pendulum and place the clock on a firm base where it is to remain. Wind it, and lift one side of the clock slightly, to set the pendulum swinging. Listen carefully to discover if the noises of the ticks are evenly spaced. If they are not, the clock will probably come to a stop, because it is 'out of beat'. Find out which way it is out of beat by gently raising one side until the clock runs evenly. It can be set in beat by bending the crutch slightly and carefully in the direction of the side that was lifted. This is done by using a finger of each hand, one above the other, on opposite sides of the crutch, and pressing. This method avoids damaging the suspension or the escapement.

A similar method is employed for longcase clocks, bending the crutch towards the quieter tick. Some clocks have a thumb screw each side of the crutch or pendulum to adjust the beat by a more refined method.

If the pendulum has a spring suspension, see that the bob swings without twisting. If its twists badly, the suspension spring will have to be renewed. Frayed or broken silk suspension should be renewed also; this is much simpler.

When transporting a weight-driven clock, which includes longcase clocks, remove the pendulum as already described. The hood of a longcase clock will have to be taken off first of all. After the pendulum, unhook the weights, noting where each came from. Those for strike and chime may be heavier than that for time train. It is wise to remove the weights when they are near the bottom of the case, or alternatively to remove them and then pull the gut lines down until they are unwound from the barrels. To do this, it will be necessary to raise the clicks by means of a screwdriver. If the seatboard on which the movement is mounted is fixed firmly, the case and movement can be carried together. If not, remove the seatboard and movement and carry them separately.

When setting up a longcase clock, make sure that the case is firm, preferably anchored to the wall by a screw through the back, or by wedges. If the case can rock, the clock will probably stop when the weights are hanging at the same length as the pendulum because they tend to swing in the opposite direction to the pendulum and abstract energy from it. Check also that the case is upright both from the front and the side. Hang the pendulum, then the weights on their pulleys. Put the hood in place to see if the dial is central, and if it is not, adjust the seatboard as required.

Give the pendulum a gentle swing to see if the clock is in beat and if necessary adjust the crutch as already explained.

M

Turn the hands to see if the clock strikes the hour indicated. If it does not, it has locking plate striking, and the locking lever should be lifted so that the strike is in phase with the time indicated. A clock with rack striking should automatically be in phase. If it is not, the hands are incorrectly fitted.

Calendar, moon and date dials are adjusted as explained in Chapter 13.

There is great joy in the possession of a genuine masterpiece of the past, clock or watch, particularly if it is in going order. It is unique, often beautiful, and almost certain to increase in value.

PART COLLECTING

Some collectors have concentrated on parts of watches. Earlier in this century there was a vogue for collecting watch cocks, which were pierced and engraved in great variety by specialist outworkers, and many fine watches were cannibalized for the purpose.

The collection of watch papers is not reprehensible as long as they are not removed from watches. During the period of the pair case in the eighteenth century, thin anti-chafing pads were placed between inner and outer cases. They were circles of cambric, lace, satin, muslin, velvet (Plate 86), or other material. Soon most watchmakers changed to paper, having their own designs printed, showing pictures, portraits, patterns, rhymes, mottoes, equation of time tables, etc., and the maker's name, or with only the maker's name (Plate 86). Some papers were also decorated by perforations and cut edges. Repairers occasionally used the backs of watch papers to record their work.

On the fringe of watch and clock collectors are those who seek the beautiful little Bilson enamelled boxes made in the shape of watch cases with proper pendants, but with dials and hands painted and fired on them.

There is some value in every type of collection – as long as no timepiece is denuded or damaged in the process, just to satisfy a fashion of the time or a collector's whim.

Appendix 1

Places where ancient vertical clocks made in England may be seen:

IRON FRAMES

Exeter cathedral (timepiece section of clock).
Marston Magna church, Somerset (preserved in gallery).
Cothele House, Calstock, Cornwall (in going order).
Ottery St Mary church, Devon (still working, astronomical dial).
Porlock church, Somerset.
Sydling St Nicholas church, Dorset (still working).
Castle Coombe church, Wiltshire.
Chilham church, Kent.

WOOD FRAMES

Leintwardine church, Herefordshire.
Sharnebrook church, Bedfordshire.
Tytherington church, Gloucestershire.

Places to see other ancient public clocks:

Salisbury cathedral (made in 1386, oldest still going).
Exeter cathedral (with astronomical dial, still working).
Wells cathedral, Somerset (clock jacks and astronomical dial. Movement in Science Museum).
Wimborne Minster, Dorset (astronomical dial, still working).
Sherborne abbey, Dorset (clock preserved in abbey).
Hampton Court, Middlesex (astronomical clock, modern movement).

Northill church, Oxfordshire (ordinary church clock, still working
 with its verge and crown wheel escapement).
Rye church, Sussex (pendulum hangs in aisle).
Wrotham church, Kent.
Wingham church, Kent.

Appendix 2

Where to see collections of clocks and watches:

Ashmolean Museum, Oxford.
Basingstoke Museum, Hampshire.
British Museum, London.
Fitzwilliam Museum, Cambridge.
Gershom Parkington Museum, Bury St Edmunds.
Guildhall Museum, City of London.
London Museum, Kensington Palace, London.
Museum of the History of Science, Oxford.
National Maritime Museum, Greenwich.
Royal Scottish Museum, Edinburgh.
Science Museum, London.
Usher Art Gallery, Lincoln.
Victoria and Albert Museum, London.
Wallace Collection, London.

Sources of information:

Horological Students' Room, British Museum, Bloomsbury, London, W.C.1.
Hon. Curator of the Library and Museum, c/o Worshipful Company of Clockmakers, Candlewick House, 116 Cannon Street, London, E.C.4.
Antiquarian Horological Society, 35 Northampton Square, London, E.C.1.
Librarian, Ilbert Library, British Horological Institute, 35 Northampton Square, London, E.C.1.

Appendix 3

Some eminent and better known makers of clocks and watches

AMANT. *Paris.* Invented pin wheel escapement *c.* 1749.

ANTHONY, WILLIAM. *London.* (*c.* 1764–1844). Fine maker.

ARNOLD, JOHN. *London.* (1736–99). One of most famous, particularly for chronometers. Also family inc. J. R. Arnold, and firm Arnold and Son, 1787–99.

ASKE, HENRY. *London.* (CC 1676–97).

BAILLON, JEAN BAPTISTE. *Paris.* (Died *c.* 1770). Famous maker.

BALDWEIN, —. *Marburg.* (Making *c.* 1563).

BANGER, EDWARD. *London.* (CC 1695–1713).

BAIN, ALEXANDER. *Edinburgh.* (Active 1838–58). Inventor electric clocks.

BARCLAY, SAMUEL. *London.* (CC 1722–51).

BARKER, WM. *Wigan.* (*c.* 1760).

BARLOW (or BOOTH), EDWARD. *London.* (1636–1716). Invented rack striking *c.* 1676.

BARRAUD, PAUL PHILIP. *London.* (Died 1820).

BARRAUD AND SONS. *Cornhill.* (1813–38). BARRAUD & LUND 1838–1842.

BARROW, NATHANIEL. *London.* (CC 1660).

BARWISE, JOHN. *London.* (Died 1842). Assoc. with Alex Bain.

BEAUVAIS, SIMON. *London.* (CC 1690–1720). Fine maker.

BECK, CHRISTOPHER. *London.* (CC 1761).

BERTHOUD, FERDINAND. *Paris.* (1727–1807). Eminent maker.

BILBIE. Somerset family of clockmakers from 1660.

BOND, WILLIAM. *Boston*, USA. Made first American marine chronometer 1812. Also family.

BORDIER. *Geneva.* Several watchmakers in this name.

BOUQUET, DAVID. *London*. (Died 1665).

BOVET, FLEURIER. Brothers made watches for Chinese market 1822–1864.

BOWYER, WILLIAM. *London*. (Active 1626–47).

BRADLEY, LANGLEY. *London*. (CC 1695). Famous maker.

BREGUET, ABRAHAM LOUIS. *Paris*. (1747–1823). Most famous watch-maker of all. Breguet & Fils from 1807 to date.

BROCKBANK. *London*. Several in 18th century and 19th century firm of BROCKBANKS, etc.

BULL, RAINULPH. *London*. (Active 1582–1617).

BÜRGI, JOBST. *Prague*. (1552–1632). Famous maker.

BUSCHMAN, DAVID. *Augsburg*. (Died 1712).

CABRIER, CHARLES. *London*. (CC 1726). Famous maker.

CARON, PETER AUGUSTE. *Paris*. (1732–99). Famous maker. Also wrote 'Barber of Seville' under name Beaumarchais.

CLAY, CHARLES. *Yorkshire and London*. (Died 1740).

CLEMENT, WILLIAM. *London*. (CC 1677). First to use anchor escapement, and steel suspension spring.

COCKEY and other spellings. Somerset family of clockmakers from *c.* 1700.

COLE, JAMES FERGUSON. *London*. (1799–1880). 'The English Breguet'.

COLLEY, RICHARD. *London*. (Died 1736).

COLSTON, RICHARD. *London*. (CC 1682–1709).

CONSTANTIN. *Geneva*. 18th century and firm VACHERON AND CONSTANTIN from 1819.

CONYERS, RICHARD. *London*. (CC 1689).

COULDRAY (COULDREY), JULIEN. *Blois*. (Died 1530). Famous maker.

COWAN, JAMES. *Edinburgh*. (Died 1781). One of most famous Scots makers.

COX, JAMES. *London*. (Died 1788). Musical and automata clocks.

COXETER, NICHOLAS. *London*. (Died 1679). Famous maker.

CRATZER, NICHOLAS. *Oxford*. (1487–1547). Clockmaker to King Henry VIII.

CRAYLE, RICHARD. *London*. (1600–71). WILLIAM. (1630–1710).

CUMMING, ALEXANDER. *Edinburgh and London*. (*c.* 1732–1814). Famous maker.

DÉBAUFRE, PETER. *London.* (CC 1689). One of watch jewel inventors. Also dead-beat verge escapement.

DELANDER, DANIEL. *London.* (CC 1699). Fine maker.

DENT, EDWARD JOHN. *London.* (1790–1853). Celebrated maker, watches, chronometers, clocks, inc. 'Big Ben'.

DONDI, JOHN. *Padua, Italy.* (1318–c. 1380). Most famous of early makers.

DROZ, PIERRE JACQUET. *La Chaux de Fonds, Switzerland.* (1721–90). Automata clocks.

DUCHESNE, CLAUDE. *London.* (CC 1693).

EARNSHAW, THOMAS. *London.* (1749–1829). Famous marine chronometer maker.

EAST, EDWARD. *London.* (c. 1610–c. 1693). Most celebrated early English maker.

ELLICOTT, JOHN. *London.* (CC 1782–95). Very fine maker.

EMERY, JOSIAH. *London.* Eminent maker and one of earliest with lever escapement.

ETHERINGTON, GEORGE. *London.* (CC 1684).

FAVRE-BULLE, FRÉDÉRIC LOUIS. *Le Locle, Switzerland.* (1770–1849). Eminent maker.

FRODSHAM. *London.* Family of able clock and watch makers from c. 1781.

FROMANTEEL, AHASUERUS. *London* (CC 1663–85). Very famous. First pendulum clocks in England.

GARON, PETER. *London.* (CC 1694).

GAUDRON, P. *Paris.* (making 1690–1730).

GORDON, ROBERT. *Edinburgh.* (making after 1703).

GOULD, CHRISTOPHER. *London.* (CC 1682). Fine maker.

GRAHAM, GEORGE. (1673–1715). *London.* One of the most eminent. Invented dead-beat escapement.

GRAY, BENJAMIN. *London.* (1676–1764).

GRETTON, CHARLES. *London.* (CC 1672). Fine maker.

GROLLER DE SERVIÈRE, NICHOLAS. *Lyons, France.* (1593–1686). Rolling ball clocks.

GRUBER, HANS. *Nuremberg.*

HABRECHT. *Strasbourg.* Family of clockmakers from 16th century. Strasbourg clock, 1571.

HALEY, CHARLES. *London*. (CC 1781–1825). Fine maker.

HARRISON, JOHN. *London*. (1693–1776). Most remarkable of all clockmakers.

HASIUS, ISAAC. *Haarlem, Holland*. Late 17th century.

HENLEIN, PETER. *Nürnberg*. (*c*. 1479–1542). First known watchmaker.

HILDEYARD, THOMAS. *Hereford and Liege*. (1690–1747).

HILL, BENJAMIN. *London*. (CC 1641).

HINDLEY, HENRY. *York*. (1701–71). Also invented screw-cutting lathe.

HOADLEY, SILAS. *Greystoke, USA*. (1786–1870). Also Samuel and Luther Hoadley. *c*. 1807.

HOLMES, JOHN. *London*. (1762–1815). Fine maker.

HOUDIN, JACQUES FRANÇOIS. *Paris*. (1783–1860). Eminent maker.

HOUGHTON, JAMES. *Ormskirk, Lancs*. (working 1800–1820).

HOURIET, JACQUES FRÉDÉRIC. *Paris and Le Locle*. (1743–1830). Fine maker.

HOWELLS, WILLIAM. *London*. (CC 1780).

HUGUENIN, ABRAM. *La Chaux de Fonds, Switzerland*. (1702–95). ABRAM LOUIS HUGUENIN, *Neuchatel*. (1733–1804).

ILBURY, WILLIAM. *London*. (Died 1839). Fine maker.

INGOLD, PIERRE FREDERICK. *Paris, London, La Chaux de Fonds*. (1787–1878). Pioneer of watch production.

JACOT, CHARLES EDOUARD. *Le Locle, Switzerland*. (working 1830).

JANVIER, ANTIDE. *Besançon, France, Paris, etc*. (*c*. 1751–1835). Very eminent.

JAPY, FRÉDÉRIC. *Beaucoust, France*. (1749–1813). Pioneer of watch production.

JAQUET-DROZ, PIERRE. *Basle, Switzerland, Paris, Madrid, etc*. (1721–1790). Celebrated maker, inc. automata.

JEROME, CHAUNCEY. *Bristol, Conn., USA* (1793–1860). Pioneer in USA.

JONES, HENRY. *London*. (CC 1663, died 1695). Very famous.

JÜRGENSEN, URBAN. *Copenhagen, Denmark*. (1776–1830). Eminent, particularly in chronometers.

KENDALL, LARCUM. *London*. (1721–95).

KETTERER, FRANZ ANTON. *Schönwald*. (1676–1750). Invented cuckoo clock.

KNIBB, JOSEPH. *Oxford and London.* (CC 1670). Also with brother John.

KNOTTESFORD, WILLIAM. *London.* (CC 1663).

LÉPINE, JEAN ANTOINE. *Paris.* (1720–1814).

LEROUX, JOHN. *London.* (CC 1781–1808). Very fine.

LEROY, JULIEN. *Paris.* (1686–1759). Very celebrated.

LEROY, PIERRE (son). *Paris.* (1717–85). Most eminent French maker.

LISTEE, THOMAS. *Halifax.* (1745–1814).

LITHERLAND, PETER. *Liverpool.* (Died 1805). Lever watch production pioneer.

LOSEBY, EDWARD THOMAS. *London.* (Died 1890). Fine chronometer maker.

LOUNDE (LOWNDES), JONATHAN. *London.* (CC 1680). Fine maker.

MCCABE, JAMES. *London.* (CC 1781). Followed by sons.

MAILLARDET, HENRI. *Fontaines and London.* (Born 1745). Automata.

MARKWICK, JAMES. *London.* (CC 1692). Fine maker.

MARKWICK–MARKHAM. Partnership of above with Robert Markwick (*c.* 1725–1805).

MASSEY, EDWARD. *London.* (1772–1825).

MEYLAN, PHILIPPE SAMUEL. *Brassus and Geneva.* (1770–1829). Automata and complicated watches.

MOORE, THOMAS. *Ipswich.* (1720–1789).

MUDGE, THOMAS. *London.* (1715–1794). Very famous. Invented lever escapement. Also Mudge & Dutton from 1759–90.

MURRAY, JAMES. *London.* (CC 1817). Fine chronometer and watchmaker.

NARDIN, ULYSSE. *Neuchatel, Switzerland.* (1823–76). Famous maker.

NEWSAM, BARTHOLOMEW. *London.* (Died 1593).

NICKALS, ISAAC. *Wells, Somerset.* (Working *c.* 1750).

NORTON, EARDLEY. *London.* (CC 1770–94). Fine maker of watches and complex clocks.

PENDLETON, RICHARD. *London.* (*c.* 1780–1808).

PERIGAL, FRANCIS. *London.* (CC 1741). And family later.

PERRON, L. *Besançon, France.* (1779–1836). Fine maker.

PINCHBECK, CHRISTOPHER. *London* (1670–1732). Fine maker of musical clocks and watches.

PRIOR, EDWARD. *London.* (1800–1868). Fine maker of watches for Turkish market. Also George Prior (1793–1830) with watches for Turkey.

QUARE, DANIEL. *London.* (1648–1742). Eminent maker.

RAINGO, M. *Paris.* Astronomical and orrery clocks.

RAMSAY, DAVID. *London.* (Died *c.* 1654). Very fine early maker.

RAYMENT, RICHARD. *Bury St Edmunds.* (Working 1743).

RECORDON, LOUIS. *London.* (1778–1824). Self-winding watch.

REID, THOMAS. *Edinburgh.* (1746–1831). Fine maker.

RENTZSCH, SIGISMUND. *London.* (1813–40).

RICHARD, DANIEL JOHN. *Neuchatel, Switzerland.* (1672–1741).

RIPPON, RICHARD. *London.* (Working 1810–24). Repeating watches.

ROBIN, ROBERT. *Paris.* (1742–1809). Famous maker.

ROGERS, ISAAC. *London.* (1754–1839). Fine maker.

ROMILLY, JOHN. *Paris.* (1714–94).

ROUSSEAU, JEAN. *London and Geneva.* (1606–84). Fine maker.

SANCAJETANO, DAVID. *Vienna.* (1726–96). Astronomical clocks.

SAVAGE, GEORGE. *Huddersfield and London.* (Working 1808–23).

SCHWILGUE, JEAN BAPTISTE. *Strasbourg.* (1776–1856). Turret clocks.

SEIGNIOR, ROBERT. *London.* (CC 1667–85). Fine maker.

SERMAND, JACQUES. *Geneva.* (1636–67).

SHORT, JAMES. *London.* (Working 1740–70).

STANTON (STAUNTON), EDWARD. *London.* (CC 1662).

STREET, RICHARD. *London.* (CC 1687).

TAYLOR. *London.* Several makers from 1640.

TERRY, ELI. *Plymouth, Conn., USA.* (1772–1853). Pioneer of clock production.

THIOUT, ANTOINE L'AÎNÉ. *Paris.* (1692–1767). Unusual clocks.

THOMAS, SETH. *Plymouth, Conn., USA* (1774–1859). Pioneer of clockmaking with Eli Terry and Silas Hoadley.

THWAITES, AINSWORTH. *London.* (CC 1751–80). Later Thwaites and Reed, still in business.

TOMPION, THOMAS. *London.* (1639–1713). Most famous English clock and watchmaker. Later Tompion and Banger (*c.* 1701) and Tompion and Graham (*c.* 1711).

VACHERON AND CONSTANTIN. *Geneva, Switzerland.* (1819–67).

VALLIN, N. *London.* (1598–1640).

VAN DER CLOESEN, BERNARD. *The Hague, Holland.* (1688–1719). Fine maker.

VAUCHER, DANIEL. *Paris.* (Making *c.* 1767–86). Eminent maker.

VAUTIER, LOYS. *Blois, France.* (1591–1638). Fine maker.

VOISIN, ANTOINE HENRY. *Paris.* (Making 1755).

VULLIAMY, JUSTIN. *London.* (1730–*c.* 90). Benjamin Lewis Vulliamy (1780–1854) was very fine maker.

WAGSTAFF, THOMAS. *London.* (1756–93).

WARD, HENRY. *Blandford.* (Making *c.* 1775–1820).

WATSON, SAMUEL. *Coventry and London.* (CC 1687–*c.* 1710). Astronomical clocks.

WEBSTER, WILLIAM. *London.* (CC 1710).

WILLARD, AARON. *Roxbury and Boston, USA* (1757–1844). Important maker. Many members of family made clocks and watches.

WILLIAMSON, JOSEPH. *London.* (Died 1725).

WINDMILLS, JOSEPH. *London.* (CC 1671). Fine maker.

Dates alone mean birth and death. *c.* means *circa* (about). CC means member of the Worshipful Company of Clockmakers.

Places given are where makers worked. Many were born elsewhere including other countries.

A full list of about 36,000 names is given in *Watchmakers and Clockmakers of the World* by G. H. Baillie (N.A.G. Press, Ltd).

The Worshipful Company of Clockmakers, London, publishes a register of apprentices from 1631 to 1931.

Appendix 4

These dates are intended only as a guide. A few are exact dates of inventions, but that does not mean to say they came into immediate use or superseded all rival systems. Often inventors and styles took as much as half a century to spread in one country. Also styles recurred in cycles.

1386	Earliest clock still working, at Salisbury Cathedral.
c. 1430	Spring drive, and therefore table clocks, introduced on continent.
c. 1490–c. 1550	English turret clocks with vertical frames.
Before 1500	Watches invented on continent.
1515	Earliest clock still telling time, at Rye church, Sussex.
c. 1550	Brass rapidly coming into use.
c. 1580	V-grooved weight pulleys introduced.
c. 1600	Lantern clocks introduced in England with balance wheel up to 1660, most with pendulum after.
c. 1600	Enamel decoration of watch dials and cases introduced.
c. 1600	Basstaille enamel introduced.
c. 1600	Watchmakers first active in London.
c. 1630	Painted enamelled watches introduced in Limoges.
c. 1630	Chain introduced for clock fusees. Gut before then.
1631	Worshipful Company of Clockmakers incorporated in London.
Before 1650	Puritan watches introduced.
c. 1650	Hooded wall clocks introduced in England.
c. 1650–c. 1700	Form watches popular.
c. 1650	Watch glasses introduced.
c. 1650	Watch cocks became round and larger.
c. 1650	Tulip pillar introduced in watch movements

c. 1650	Minute hands began to appear gradually.
1657	Pendulum clock invented. Endless rope (or chain) winding invented.
c. 1660	Silvering of brass introduced.
c. 1660–*c.* 1700	Architectural style English clocks. Convex moulding under hoods of longcase clocks. Winged cherub spandrels on dials.
c. 1660–*c.* 1725	Ebony veneer for English cases.
c. 1665–*c.* 1820	Longcase clocks in production in England.
c. 1665–1670	Rising hood on longcase clocks.
c. 1670	Flinqué enamel on watches.
c. 1670	Chain introduced for watch fusees. Gut before that.
c. 1671	Anchor escapement invented. Long pendulum introduced.
c. 1675	Waistcoat with watch pocket introduced.
c. 1675	Balance spring for watches invented.
c. 1675	Pair watch cases introduced.
c. 1675–*c.* 1700	Olive wood (oyster pieces) veneer for English clock cases.
c. 1675–1700	Ten-inch dials for longcase clocks. Before that smaller, after larger – 14-inch from *c.* 1800.
c. 1676	Rack striking invented and repeating for clocks.
Before 1700	Huaud family of watch enamellers active.
c. 1685	Gold watch cases marked (inc. date letter) by Worshipful Company of Goldsmiths.
1687	Repeating watch invented.
c. 1690–*c.* 1760	Burr walnut veneered English clock cases.
Before 1700	Night clocks introduced.
Before 1700– after 1750	Marquetry popular for English clock cases.
Before 1700	Watches with unorthodox dials tried out.
Before 1700	Bolt and shuttle maintaining power invented.
Before 1700– *c.* 1800	Coach clocks like large watches.
c. 1700–*c.* 1760	Lacquered English clock cases.
c. 1700	Pendulum watch introduced.
c. 1700	Egyptian pillars introduced for watch movements.
After 1700	Dutch Zaandam bracket clocks introduced.
After 1700	Break arch dial in use on English clocks.

1715	Dead-beat escapement invented. Regulators began to be more in demand.
c. 1715	French balloon clock introduced.
1721	Mercury pendulum invented.
1724	Harrison invented special maintaining power.
c. 1725	Dust caps common on watch movements.
c. 1725–*c.* 1750	Repoussé cased watches popular.
c. 1725	Cylinder escapement perfected.
After 1725	Front pendulum introduced on Black Forest clocks.
1730	Gridiron pendulum invented.
c. 1740	Silver watch cases marked (inc. date letter) by Worshipful Company of Goldsmiths.
c. 1740	Cuckoo clocks first made, in Black Forest.
After 1740	Mahogany used for English clock cases.
c. 1740–*c.* 1790	Pagoda top introduced for English clocks.
1741	Pin-wheel escapement invented in France.
c. 1750	Round dials introduced for bracket and table clocks.
c. 1750	French regulators with glass doors in favour.
c. 1750	French skeleton clocks introduced.
c. 1750	Shield clocks introduced in Black Forest.
c. 1750	Dutch staartklok introduced.
c. 1750	White enamelled watch dials popular.
c. 1750–*c.* 1820	English provincial clockmakers most prolific producers of longcase clocks.
After 1750	Halifax moon introduced on English longcase clocks.
c. 1760	Swan neck pediments to English clock cases.
After 1760	Gravity escapement for clocks.
1770	Lever escapement invented. Did not come into general use until nearly 1800.
1770	Barred watch movement introduced.
Before 1775– *c.* 1810	English balloon clock.
c. 1775	Tidal dials popular in longcase clocks.
After 1775	Painted dials used on longcase clocks.
1776	Centre seconds (jumping) hand for watches invented.
c. 1780	Self-winding watch invented.
c. 1780–*c.* 1800	Virgule escapement in French watches.
c. 1790	Lancet top English clock case introduced.
c. 1790–*c.* 1870	Duplex escapement in English watches

N

1797–8	Act of Parliament clocks.
1798	Pin lever watch escapement invented (L. Perron).
Before 1800	Round glass doors introduced for English table clocks.
Before 1800	Tell-tale watchman's clock invented.
Before 1800	Rack lever escapement (invented 1722) in English watches.
Before 1800	Marine chronometers developed.
c. 1800	English Dial clocks introduced.
c. 1800	Picture frame clocks being made in France.
c. 1800	Production of wooden clocks in USA.
c. 1800	Single watch case superseding pair case.
c. 1800	Guillochet enamelled watch cases introduced.
c. 1800	Ormskirk escapement introduced.
After 1800	French carriage clocks introduced.
After 1800	Swiss musical watches introduced.
After 1800	Vienna regulator introduced.
1801	Tourbillon watch invented.
1802–60	Banjo clock made in USA.
1808	Congreve rolling ball clock invented.
c. 1810	Mahogany-cased regulators with glass doors became popular.
c. 1810	Chamfer top table clock case introduced.
After 1810	English copy French Empire clock styles.
1818	Waggon spring clock introduced in USA.
c. 1820	Keyless winding introduced for watches.
c. 1820–30	Watch ticking 5 times a second introduced. (Almost universal today).
c. 1830–*c.* 1860	French made animated three-dimensional automaton clocks.
c. 1837–*c.* 1910	Victorian copies of Regency clocks. English cottage clocks, and sedan clocks made.
c. 1830–1836	French gothic style revival.
c. 1840	English skeleton clocks introduced.
1842	Button hand setting for watches invented.
1849	Brocot visible escapement introduced.
c. 1850	Chinese duplex escapement invented.
c. 1850–*c.* 1870	Germans make animated picture clocks.
c. 1850	First electric clocks, but not made in numbers until after 1900.

c. 1850	Brocot perpetual calendar introduced.
1858	Trumpeter clocks made in Black Forest.
1859	Westminster chimes introduced.
1860	Hipp electric master clocks introduced.
c. 1862	Centre second hand that can be returned to zero invented.
c. 1865	Roscopf watch invented.
1874	Standard Time Co. introduced electric clock systems.
c. 1875	Postmans' alarms made in Black Forest.
c. 1875	Pocket chronometers become popular.
c. 1875	Carved mahogany longcase clocks over 9 feet with tubular chimes popular.
c. 1880	Novelty rocking clock, held by woman or elephant, and others introduced.
c. 1880	400-day clock introduced.
1880–1896	Waterbury watches made in USA.
c. 1880	Introduction of Industrial Revolution clocks in form of beam engines, lighthouses, ships at sea, etc.
1894	Karrusel watch invented.
After 1900	Bulle electric clock introduced.
1905	Ticket-clock introduced.
1906	Eureka electric clock introduced.

Index

Index

Index

Index